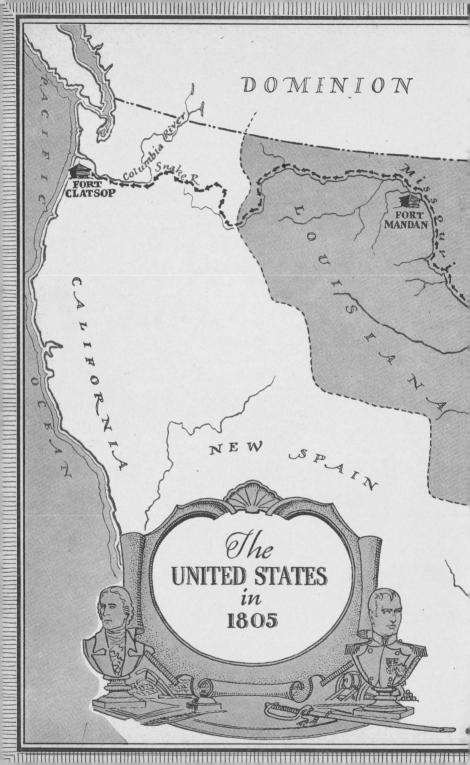

DOMINION OF CANADA

ROCKY

Maria's R.

GREAT
FALLS

Missouri River

LITTLE BELT
MOUNTAINS

Judith's

TES of the
UNTAINS

Musselshell River

Yellowstone River

FORT
MANDAN

HREE FORKS

BOZEMAN
PASS

Gallatin R.

Jefferson R.

Madison R.

MOUNTAINS

Yellowstone
Lake

BIG HORN
MOUNTAINS

GRAND TETONS

WIND RIVER
MOUNTAINS

Shoshone
Reservation
Agency

FORT BRIDGER
Great Treaty 1868

UINTAH
MOUNTAINS

Green River

C.V.J.

FORWARD THE NATION

by Donald Culross Peattie

DONALD CULROSS PEATTIE

Forward the Nation

G. P. PUTNAM'S SONS, NEW YORK

Designed by Robert Josephy

MANUFACTURED IN THE UNITED STATES OF AMERICA

FOREWORD

THE AUTHOR wishes expressly to state that none of the characters in this book is fictional, and that there is nothing in the least coincidental about any resemblances to actual facts and persons. On the contrary, he affirms that the events of this narrative are all true. After long study of original sources, and travel to the scenes of incidents here related, he found it necessary to invent not one happening, individual, locality, trait, or property. All were provided by the unimpeachable reports of eye-witnesses, and the official records of the United States government.

On the other hand, the author makes no claim to have written a history of the Lewis and Clark expedition, nor yet a biography of Sacajawea; these tasks were done by those best fitted for them. He respectfully disclaims the honor of the historian's rank, and its obligations as well. Yet he has nowhere, to his knowledge, distorted fact. Whatever he has recounted here that is not stated in the records he believes can be discovered there between the lines.

FORWARD THE NATION

❧ I

THE COURSE of a nation can be pictured as a great river system. On the map that looks like the outline of a tree. But it is nothing like a tree, which grows up from its trunk into its branches. A river grows downward from high places, uniting its streams into one great channel. So it is with a nation.

In our system every least rivulet may give as much water as any other. Wherever we are, upon the current, a multitude of springs have gushed forth to give us this flotation. We are all borne along on the determined flood, yet it is we, the many, who direct it.

This story traces one single, slender tributary to the American course. In remote western wastes it first broke purely from the undiscovered rock. Swift and bright and singing, it could never, you would think of it then, carry anything but a feather or a leaf. For this life was only an Indian woman's. But while the stream of it is still no more than a brook, it plunges, precipitate as chance, into our main waters. It guides the green young torrent of our progress, through unknown mountain passes; it sets the current, it forwards the nation.

3

So this stream engraves the land forever. So, at its end, it does not die in the sea; it becomes immortal as the ocean deeply breathing with its tides.

The tale begins where first, as a rivulet, this life-stream catches the light of history. In a year of lauded wars and hidden treaties, there happened, far off in the hot interior of our own continent, a small personal violence, now significant to us all. It happened unheeded among a tribe who keep no records and have no long memory, to the little girl whose life has now come sparkling and dancing out of its mountain birthplace toward inconceivable destiny.

The scene of this trifling pillage is the meeting point of three shallow rivers. They have at that time no name in English, for that tongue is not spoken within two thousand miles of the Three Forks. The year is 1800, the season that hot month when thunderclouds pile up behind the Bitterroots and the berries are ripe at the Three Forks of the Missouri.

That summer there were thunderclouds all over Europe; they threatened America too. Yet it was a good summer, in Nature's way; never, wrote Thomas Jefferson, had he seen such a fine wheat crop on the fields of Monticello. As for the harvest of Napoleon's victories, it was piled the higher with his new mastery over Italy. But in his mouth already there was a first foretaste of ashes, even as he knelt in Milan Cathedral to hear the *Te Deum* he had ordered in celebration of his latest triumph at Marengo.

It may have been on the very day of that famous battle that Sacajawea came, unsuspecting as a little Proserpina, to pick berries at the Three Forks. They would have been hard red serviceberries, chokecherries that it takes an Indian to swallow with a straight face, dark-staining winy elderberries and, best of all, the golden currants that must have slipped sweetly down the child's thirsty throat.

Sacajawea, whose name means Canoe Launcher, was twelve years old in 1800, at the meeting place of the shallow courses that make the great river. She was a Shoshone of the Lemhi band, from the western slopes of the Bitterroots. A year ago she must have been a *dzidzi*, a girl child, the most naked and inconsiderable possession of her elders. Now she had the dignity of deerskin skirt and blouse, and her blue-black hair was combed and braided; she was a *náivi*, a young girl.

But girlhood, in the life of a little savage virgin, is brief. Twelve, thirteen, fourteen years of age, these are the summers we would recognize in her as girlhood. Then, for a season short as a grass-flower's, she laughs. Not the crow-like cackle of the old squaws, who laugh out of bitterness, but the gaiety of one who has a little privilege, a little value in the tents of her father—the trading price, if she is really pretty, of ten horses. After that, children who come like the seeds of the cottonwood on a June wind, until she is withered. And the pack for her back, fifty pounds, and sixty, in day-long marches, till she dies.

Sacajawea at twelve years old had pride; she had young beauty; even white men later called her beautiful. In the tribe her father stood high, and she had been promised in marriage; her price in horseflesh was already paid. Now she stood, the rye grass tall about her, running the berries from her brown hand into her basket; the sun was hot on her head, and its sparkle on the river was sharp in her eyes. She could see the boys who had ridden down from the Lemhi pass watering their horses there, slouched at rest on the beasts that gratefully sucked the ripples. She could hear the other girls chattering at a little distance in the grove. The cottonwoods were whispering above her, passing rumors, conspiring innocently, laughing covertly. The smell of a river bottom came pleasantly to her nostrils, all the sweet, decaying, mucky odor of a place where cattails and bulrushes grow. There was a little flock of mallards making out from under the bushes, across a quiet sheet of water, for the opposite shore, and she thought that if one of the boys had been near enough, she could have called to him to come and shoot them, and there would have been duck for dinner. A single swallow was skimming in the hot sunlight; the rest, at nesting under the shadowed cool of the cliffs, would not rise at this hour unless something disturbed them.

Looking east downstream, she put the back of her hand up above her eyes to shade them, for the light glittered on the water where it ran faster with conjoined volume. Here begins the longest arm of the greatest river system in the northern hemisphere. From this place where it dazzled the young Shoshone's eyes, it flowed out of the country of her people, "the people with horses," gathering tributaries from the lands of the Blackfeet, the people with guns, and from the lands of the Teton Sioux. Braiding and weaving, this flood ate its way east and down the slope of the Great Plains, past the earthen lodges of the dancing Mandans, turning south, carving ancient loesses, forever engulfing its own banks, choked with its load of silts and logs and buffalo carcasses, through the country of the Kiowas and Poncas and Osages, till it boiled out, strong and dirty, into the shorter, clearer stream of the Mississippi.

Our people, from the Illinois shore, from their frontiers, have seen this debouching of the Missouri. But they do not know where the river rises. No citizen of the sixteen United States has ever seen the Rockies, the "stony mountains" as Mr. Jefferson writes of them, the "shining mountains" that the Sieur de Verendrye glimpsed in 1742, before he had to turn back, beaten. We only knew, in those days, that the Rockies were there, a rumored threat in stone and ice, a wall across our future.

Behind those mountains Sacajawea had been born, in the valley of the Lemhi which feeds the Salmon that whirls, the River of No Returning, through sheer canyons into the Snake. The twisting Snake rolls into the Columbia that sweeps down through basalt palisades and the dunes that storm across them, taking its lordly way through the Cascades, where the giant canoe cedars grow, until it sweeps out, into the cold fogs of the north Pacific.

Sacajawea's people, salmon-eaters once cooped up in the valleys of Idaho, had become "the people with horses" ever since a halfbreed Spanish trader brought from the Southwest mounts whose distant sires may have been Coronado's Arabians. So the Lemhi Shoshones now could sally forth from the mountains, eastward over the Lemhi pass and out on the plains where the Sioux and Blackfeet hunted the buffalo. In those days the galloping Sioux had scarcely begun to gallop; they ran on their hard soles. But the Lemhi Shoshones rode—like madmen on their naked horses—when they hunted. And they were envied by the plains tribes as men envy demons.

Therefore danger loomed, as clouds forever loom up over Montana's mountains, where Sacajawea idled among the currant bushes. She was living her last moments as a Shoshone girl, held in the great hot bubble of the world she knew—the plains, the mountains, and the free high sky.

There was a sudden scurry in the poplar thickets, and the swallows were flung out from their cliff like a wind-whipped blanket. Peeping and warning, they swirled up on some unfelt advancing blast and scattered. Then the Pah-kes, the Knife River band of Minnetarees, burst into the clearing with a yell, and leaped for the horses.

There is only one record of that short struggle; it

comes at second hand to us, like an echo thrown back from the cliff. It reports that the Shoshone boys did what any Indian might have done; they saved the horses, by riding them off at a gallop, and left the berry-picking girls to shift for themselves. Girls would not be killed, nor in the hands of the enemy would they be dangerous. So Sacajawea fled unprotected, but in the shallows of midstream the brutal hands took her.

For a few minutes the swallows were kept aloft in angry disturbance by the screams, the splashing, and all the human commotion along the river. They flew round and round, rose and sank, and passed each other complaining of outrage in bird shrieks.

Then the Pah-kes were gone, running their captives before them, on the first leg of a pitiless journey hundreds of miles down the river, to the east, to the Mandan villages. How the eyes of the young Mandan men would light up to see these girls for sale! But the old wives of the rich men would egg them on to the bidding; a slave girl in the lodge meant labor lightened. There would be a wagering and a playing of game-sticks around the campfires. There would be hungry laughter and fighting, and yells of triumph and of loss, and each captive would be wagered in pieces—her beads, her skirt, her blouse, her moccasins, her body.

The swallows were soon settled down again at peace, at the Three Forks of the Missouri. For a long time the cottonwoods chattered, but there was no one to listen to their whispers and rumors. The spot was empty—it might be empty for a long time to come, for Indians remember places where their tribe has suffered humiliation, and avoid them.

But this place Sacajawea never forgot. It was branded upon her memory as the last view of her homeland she gazed upon, confident of the ground under her feet, the last place where, with a young girl's pride, she had belonged to herself.

And it was a spot strategic in all the story to come, the story of the greatest exploration in American history. It was the threshold to the pass for which the mind of Thomas Jefferson often groped. A few days after his election as President of the United States, he sat writing in his Monticello study, the room with the old worn globe in it, and the mockingbird that was allowed to hop about, out of its cage. He is writing to Meriwether Lewis, Esq., Captain of the First Regiment of Infantry, stationed at Detroit, inviting him to become his private secretary. "Your knowledge of the Western Country . . ." flows the pen ". . . capacity to contribute to the mass of information which it is interesting to the administration to acquire. . . ."

The enterprise which both writer and recipient have conceived is secret still, but the pen is whispering of it to the clock, across the page preserved today among the Jefferson papers in the Library of Congress. And the clock ticks off the minutes. The old year is passing; the Federalist party is passing; the ropes that bound us to a narrow past are loosening. The adventure of which the stolen Indian girl is to be heroine already is floated. The expedition, so long dreamed by Jefferson and Lewis, built like a ship by their two minds, has slipped from its moorings. The tide of irresistible events is murmuring, tugging, about its keel. The course is westward, but so quietly does the voyage begin that, aboard or elsewhere, it is hardly noticed that the anchor is up.

☙ II

IN OCTOBER of that year, when the Mandans were getting in their harvest of corn and squash at the great bend of the Missouri, a mighty game of power politics was in progress, thousands of miles away from the great stakes. At San Ildefonso, France was playing against Spain, for "Louisiana"—all the land between the Mississippi and the Rockies on the distant American continent.

At this moment the shadow of crafty hands seems to fall all across the vast board upon the little pawn, Sacajawea. But it is only a passing shadow. For the credulous Charles IV of Spain has but the shadow of a claim, and Bonaparte wins but the shadow of a possession.

All the same, Lucien Bonaparte preened himself as the ink dried on his signature confirming the treaty that ceded Louisiana to France. At a stroke of the pen he had won more land than was lost in the calamity of the Egyptian campaign by that vaunting elder brother he represented, who called himself not only "General Bonaparte" but "First Consul." An imitation of the

Romans, that "consul"! An imitation of Alexander, that campaign.

Haunted indeed by the old Alexandrine dream, the opaque gaze of the First Consul was fixed upon the East. Egypt, Persia, India! Feverishly his eyes turned toward an Orient he had never seen and did not understand. All he knew of it was its sphinx-like smile, its pearls and perfumes. He talked of his continental policy, his new order for Europe, but the war in Egypt had been only an attempted step toward India. Yet while England kept the seas he could not carry his pseudo-Roman eagles of bronze beyond the Indus, to overwhelm with his magnificence those ancient peoples who had seen a hundred conquerors and survived them all. And for the East Napoleon lusted, like a jaded young sensualist for the arms of one older, many-jeweled, able to teach all enervations.

Thomas Jefferson, third president of a nation twenty-five years old, turned his long back to the East. He looked westward; he dreamed toward the West. His thoughts like living eagles went shining over the Blue Ridge. They were youth looking for its future. While Boone was cutting our way through Kentucky, the thoughts of his President flew over him, so high and swift they cast no shadows. They passed him and went on, across the Father of Waters to the grandfather of them all, the Missouri. They rose soaring over the wall of the Rockies, and over the Spanish deserts, till the western ocean crawled beneath them.

Jefferson so pondered, resting from the fatigues of a year and a half in office, amid the summer beauties of Monticello. But rumors ran through his mind like the winds that troubled the trees above him. For two years the French and Spanish ambassadors had been denying them. But on the first of October the President received definite information of that treaty so secretly signed at San Ildefonso two years ago to this day. Louisiana was in Napoleon's possession! At once Mr. Jefferson ordered his horse saddled and brought to the door.

Wildair fretted and sidled before the portico. This first day of fall was fresh as sparkling wine just decanted; the prickle of it made the beast blow out his nostrils. His restless hoofs did a shadow dance upon the driveway. He tossed his head, and the black boy at the bridle had to leap a little, and laughed. Their master strode down the steps, and Wildair whinnied like a far away bugle.

The black boy set his muscular leg for Jefferson to mount; there was a leathern creaking of the saddle, and the horse, taking the noble weight, arched his head proudly. Out of the door old Caesar hurried, bringing his master's dispatch box. This was fixed behind the saddle; Wildair shifted, coaxing for action. The gloved hand touched his neck, the heels clapped his sides, and he stepped off smoothly, a covey of black children scattering at the roadside. The white dome of Monticello retreated into its green peace.

The Blue Ridge had come clear out of its doldrum

mists. The oaks today hung out ragged flags of red and yellow, and there was a low running fire of garnet in the blueberry bushes. Wildair rolled the white of his eyes at a squirrel humping across the road, scorning to shy at a trifle so familiar. He knew his American autumn as well, in his own way, as his rider knew it. And Wildair knew every road and where it led, just as his master did. This one went to James Monroe's Ashlawn, that to Madison's Montpelier. Another led toward the old Clark place, where George Rogers Clark and his brother William were born; another went to Locust Hill, home of Meriwether Lewis. The roads that Wildair used to travel in northern Virginia will carry you back to the origins of the nation.

But today's road ran northeastward, and Wildair knew it by the dispatch box hard on his heaving back. He settled into the long even pace of a horse that has far to go, but disdains to plod a step of it.

So travels the third president of the United States. King George goes bowling in his satin-lined coach; Napoleon rides surrounded by his guards, rightly afraid of assassination; the Emperor of Cathay is borne on the backs of his fellow man. Thomas Jefferson rode alone on Wildair, his little dispatch box of state papers behind him, the red mud of Virginia flying backward from the strong hoofs.

The Blue Ridge sank away in the west, and the Piedmont pines came forward, whispering, to meet him. All through the shadowed Wilderness they softly swayed and chanted, watching the rider pass. At Fredericks-burg, where the ships from France and England docked, he smelled bland tidewater on the air. Here he could rest again for the night, and the horse heave his sides free of the girth. Then the long, pulling muscles under the bright hide carry Jefferson on again. Though the heels are pressing in Wildair's flanks, the journey takes four days—past Quantico among its marshes, and Mount Vernon on its hills, through mossy Alexandria. At last, when the day is waning, the White House comes in sight, standing in grave prophetic grace among the few brick houses near enough to be neighbors. Wildair stood blowing, as his rider dismounted and hastened in, bidding the servant at the door send his secretary to him in his office.

This was a large room having a long table down the center of it, broad enough for unrolled maps and spread papers, with drawers in each side where Mr. Jefferson kept his favorite gardening tools. Maps and charts were on the walls between the book shelves; the old globe, brought here from Monticello, loomed softly like a planet appearing in the twilight sky. The mockingbird was also here; it spoke a greeting from its hanging cage, and Jefferson, whistling answer, set open the little barred door.

The mocker shot out to freedom, following the President's retreating back in a long swoop, and swerved with a flutter as a servant entered with the dispatch box. From the top of a bookcase the bird watched while the black man set candles burning and answered in a rich dark chuckle what his master asked; then, when the room was left blooming silently with soft flowers of light, the mocker peered, inquisitive to see what his tamer was doing.

Hands clasped behind him, head as always thrust in eagerness a little forward of his rangy body, Jefferson was studying a map on the wall, a map of young America. Now he put his hands up on each side of it; they framed it, cupped it, kept away any claim from both its shores.

The map pictured the United States upon a continent whose full spread was not yet even imagined by the cartographer. Virginia lay ample, a great breeding ground for great men; Maine belonged to potent little Massachusetts. Tennessee was there, a daughter of the federation not thirteen years old; Kentucky was even younger. What of the Deep South was as yet in the union was largely Georgia, based on a narrow strip marked in spidery letters, "Mississippi Territory." That vast field of opportunity, watered by the Ohio river, was the Northwest Territory, all the way to the Mississippi. Beyond that, straying across unmeasured immensity, sprawled letters that announced, "Louisiana Territory." Vaguely the maker of the map had tinted these reaches yellow, color of Spain; the same ochre stained the Floridas, that compassed all the lazy bayous of the Gulf. Paling uncertainly, the ochre ran all the way to a California with an oddly crabbed coastline.

This other side of a continent, unknown as the far side of the moon and greater than the known part, was pictured in timid dimensions. America, as it lay pinned there against the White House wall, was but half unfolded.

Jefferson moved a thoughtful hand to travel down the broadening Mississippi to New Orleans, gate city for the West. Yesterday he had believed New Orleans Spanish. And from Madrid America had long ago received permission to use that port freely. But now New Orleans belonged to Bonaparte. Instead of a lax Spain, a plotting France had its hands upon the windpipe of the West.

The West! Jefferson's deep-sunk eyes went broodingly to it on the map. Ten years ago there had been no Americans west of the Appalachians but trappers, traders, and fugitives. Today seven million dollars' worth of commerce flowed down the "western waters" through New Orleans to foreign markets. In all the broad opening lands ran only the one great highway of the waters, carrying the flatboats and broadhorns southward. The West must keep that way free to the sea, or die.

Jefferson believed in the West, as the West believed in him. He put his faith in the common man, the man with one axe, one rifle, one woman, one God, one mule, one vote. Adding one vote to another, those common men had swept Thomas Jefferson into the presidency.

Upon the panels of the door sounded his secretary's

rap. "Come in!" The President turned from the map, his face breaking into warmth.

Meriwether Lewis crossed the room to him with the rapidity of affection. As they met in greeting, Lewis, with his military ease, his gold fob dangling, his head alert above the smartly wound white stock, looked almost a young dandy beside the casual elder man in his so simple dress.

"I shall want notices dispatched by messenger tonight to all the cabinet members," the President was directing. "Of an immediate meeting to consider the situation. And we must write to Livingston in Paris at once."

Between the two men talking ran visibly an understanding sympathetic as that between father and son. From boyhood in Albemarle County, Lewis had known the elder man and venerated him. Jefferson's shadow was already long when Lewis began to grow in it, the shadow of a giant who wrote the Declaration of Independence at only thirty-three. Meriwether was seven, old enough to savor excitement, when Tarleton's Redcoats came to Monticello to capture Governor Jefferson, and that revolutionary watched them coolly from a hill through his spyglass, as they vainly milled about.

When the Lewises removed to the pine forests of Georgia, the lad became a stout woodsman and expert hunter, growing already into one of those silent men who love the wilderness more than any woman. At thirteen he went to the school of the Reverend Doctor Maury where, years ago, young Tom Jefferson had studied. Ambassador Jefferson then was far away in France, fighting for the freedom of the seas—against France, against England, against the Barbary pirates.

Now it was Bonaparte, and Talleyrand with his dreams of New World empire, that Jefferson must fight.

"Already France has got one foot in our door," he concluded to Lewis.

"Here in the capital," agreed his secretary, "we hear how uneasy the country is, with talk of war to come."

"The Federalists perhaps fear that it won't," the President dryly remarked. "You must inform Mr. Madison in the morning that I beg he will wait upon me as soon as convenient. If possible, we must at once begin efforts to buy from Bonaparte New Orleans and the Floridas, at least."

"But the West, sir," Lewis impulsively said. "Is France to be allowed to hold so vast a portion of America?"

Jefferson looked at him with intent appreciation. Young Meriwether Lewis was the only other man who seriously entertained his own bold idea concerning that great unknown West.

"Gently, my boy, we must go gently," he warned. "War must be avoided. By just negotiation, by the enterprise that you and I have conceived together, we may yet establish our claim to the West."

And the minds of both flashed back nearly ten years to a moment when they had thus faced one another, when each saw burning in the other's eyes the scheme of carrying the American flag out to the far Pacific and so claiming for their country all the wild terrain from the Mississippi to the western sea. Jefferson had then just proposed such an expedition to the American Philosophical Society in Philadelphia; among those interested was George Washington, who subscribed the largest sum, twenty-five dollars. Meriwether Lewis, a lad of eighteen in the militia, got word of the project which for years he himself had been hatching in the private glory-world where boys plan out the deeds they do as men. He hastened to present himself before the Secretary of State, the old family friend of Albemarle County.

Jefferson must have smiled a little at the slim figure not broadened to majority as yet, facing him erect and confident, betraying intensity by the pressure of the fingers upon the table between them. He shook his graying sandy head a little.

"Eighteen is young to weigh all dangers," he told the boy. "And this, I venture to say, is the most dangerous mission on which any American ever set out alone."

"Alone?"

"Almost. I have proposed to the Society," Jefferson told him matter-of-factly, "that the person engaged should be attended by a single companion only, to avoid exciting alarm among the Indians."

"I accept that condition!" cried the boy.

Jefferson bent forward across his desk to look at him keenly. "I believe you," he admitted. Then he leaned back and, dropping his voice into kindly refusal, added,

"I believe that were you ten years older you might attempt it and succeed."

Well, Lewis *was* ten years older now. The earlier attempt had failed, and suddenly, urgently, appeared a need for success. To Lewis opportunity all at once flamed incandescent.

"Sir," he said on a hot breath of ardor, "you know my readiness for the enterprise. I have worked out plans for it to the last detail. My one request would be that I might name my second in command."

"Are there then two of you at once so rash and yet so able?" the President asked with smiling interest.

"Under Wayne, sir, in my division was an officer who is the one man who, with myself, could get through to the western ocean. William Clark. I vouch for him, Mr. President, as for myself."

Jefferson clapped him on the shoulder. "I accept him. But the time is not ready, boy. The wheels of state groan slowly. Now we must come back from our scheme of great adventure to drudgery, I fear." He searched in his dispatch box. "Here are some letters I have drafted. Will you at once make me fair copies?"

Lewis took the papers and sat down to write. Jefferson, still standing—for it is good to stand after four days in the saddle—picked up a packet of official papers to glance through, but his eyes strayed to his serious young secretary bent over the traveling quill. What a sword, exulted the statesman, to have at one's right hand! At birth the finest elements were blent in the metal, he thought. In the fires of frontier danger it had been tempered; light swift strokes of experience had shaped it. It was sharp, lithe, long, flashing—a blade, some would have misjudged, best suited to diplomacy, love, philosophy or science. To cut down a tree, to clear a track in the wilderness, one does not ordinarily employ a rapier. Yet Jefferson meant so to employ it. For he foresaw that a way to the Pacific could not be hacked. Nothing could pass through the mountains, the alien tribes, the rapids, but a resilient will and a shining intelligence.

You can buy an axe man and his axe any time, and let him blunder. But to find under your hand a man shaped to your purpose by the single thought of his lifetime, is the rarest of luck. Or else the prevision of genius.

☙ III

LUCIEN BONAPARTE jumped from his carriage in the courtyard of the Tuileries, and went bounding up the steps. The huge old palace, so long grimly empty of life, was flooded with new fortune, refurnished by its mistress with a taste lush as her native tropics, in a style hatched by those Roman eagles of Napoleon's into a bastard classic grandeur. Lucien hastened down the long corridors, past busts on marble columns, colossal vases set on pedestals, furniture monstrous with griffin claws and gilt sphinx heads, and, reaching an ultimate inner splendor, was told that the master of all this, of most of Europe, was in his bath.

Over the valet's murmur rose a lordly voice behind shut doors: "That brother of mine? Let him in."

Lucien entered, into a cloud of perfumed steam that rolled to the high ceiling like smoke from the battle scenes pictured on the wallpaper.

"Good morning!" The ironically fraternal greeting was full of a bathroom resonance. The hero of Marengo lolled at full length in an opaque solution of suds and eau de Cologne. That face which looked to Lucien usually as if it were cut out of cold gray stone, was given by the water's heat a flush that in this intimacy suggested the sensuous strain which had delivered Napoleon into the fat white hands of the widow Beauharnais. But the deep eyes were hard and dark. So Lucien, he himself records, turned away, put off his purpose, chatted nervously, while distrust and dislike ran like ice and fire through the linked Corsican blood. Lucien was waiting for Joseph; together, they had agreed, they must confront their upstart brother with outrageous rumor. No sooner did Joseph appear than the great military genius, soaping his neck, took the attack out of their hands. Calmly he announced the rumor as a fact. He was selling off Louisiana for the sinews of war.

"I flatter myself," Lucien said, closing both fists on his control, "that the Chambers will not give their consent."

"You flatter yourself!" The sneer was open now. "*C'est précieux, en vérité!*"

Joseph put in his oar; the voices rose; the valet fussed in terror over the warming towels; to his poor head, swimming in the heat and vapor, the battle on the wallpaper seemed to come alive. His master's voice lifted above the others made him shudder.

"Well, Monsieur Joseph, Citizen Lucien, think of it what you will. Go into mourning for your blessed treaty, brother. You, Joseph, you twitch like an old woman in fear for your sacred Constitution. But I shall do without the consent of anyone at all. Now do you understand?"

Joseph, coloring up like a turkey with anger and with heat, leaned over the tub and promised, "I'll lead the opposition."

Napoleon laughed in his red face.

"Laugh, laugh, then!" sputtered Joseph. "You shall yet stand before me on the tribune!"

His brother made a sound of mirth colder and more dangerous, and rose half out of his bath. "It is your opposition that I laugh at!" He stood, crouched and naked like a beast, gripping the tub, the water running off his taut white body, his voice deadly. "This project, conceived by me, negotiated by me, shall be ratified and executed by me alone!"

"Good!" shouted Joseph, lost to rage. "Then you, and I, and all of us that the Republic may hold responsible for this betrayal of its rights, may prepare to go and join the poor devils you've sent to a tropic prison-hell."

"Insolence!" Napoleon started forward as if he would leap at his brother's throat. Then suddenly he threw himself back in the bath, and a sheet of soapy water flew into Joseph's face, drenching him and Lucien to the skin. Napoleon burst into a shout of laughter, and all at once the three again were the boys that had romped together on Ajaccio's rocky shores. The valet —so history pauses on its stately march to notice—quietly crumpled in his corner in a dead faint.

Thus casually did Napoleon decide, as he lightly put it, to commit Louisianicide. Behind Talleyrand's back, without the knowledge or approval of the French people, he meant to toss away what was theirs, in more of his insensate gambles on the battlefield.

In the very month of his decision, the port of New Orleans was suddenly closed to American shipping. No longer would the lean, keen men down from the western states and opening territories come in their broadhorns and flat-boats to thread an easy way along the levees. As the President announced the news to his cabinet, the faces turned toward him showed astonishment, indignation, comprehension. A crafty thumb was pressing, pressing, upon that windpipe of the West!

Fear of war grew in the country. Choked at New Orleans, would the West force hostilities with France? Such a war was the aim of the foreign policy of the Federalists. For then, too, there were men in the land who hated the President more than possible foreign enemies.

So they listened, eager for the snick of long rifles cocking. The men of Kentucky, Ohio, Tennessee, were men of action, and the eastern gentlemen, who had despised them, now urged them on to act. If the President refused the westerners the right to strike for liberty, would they not set up their own independent nation, across the Alleghenies? Then would be the moment for New England secession! And that was the secret core of the Federalist domestic policy.

27

Suddenly the Federalists had discovered the West. Oh, yes, they were very solicitous now of its prosperity; they were touchy for it about its honor. Trans-Appalachian men, they cried, were not a breed to suffer betrayal. Why didn't they seize New Orleans? Why didn't the President do something? Why did he not tell the country his plans, take us into his confidence? What this country lacked was leadership!

As for Mr. Jefferson, he let the mockingbird out of its cage and, while it hopped upon the table, he dictated a letter to Mr. James Monroe. Ships were too slow, seas were too wide, to wait upon a correspondence with the ambassador in Paris. No, what was needed there was a man who so knew the President's own mind that he could act without advices. "Our object," dictated Jefferson to his secretary, "in purchasing New Orleans and the Floridas is a measure liable to assume so many shapes that no instructions could be squared to fit them." As he took down these words, the eyes of Meriwether Lewis shone.

So lovely Mrs. Monroe began to make plans for the visit to dear Paris again. How happy the girls would be to see their old schoolmate, Hortense Beauharnais!

Hortense was promised now in marriage to Napoleon's brother Louis. This was a scheme of her mother's; Josephine's purpose in it was to hold her husband. She was too old now to bear him a child, but if Hortense produced an heir, Napoleon might forget his sternest excuse for a divorce. And the threat of losing him haunted Josephine's days and troubled her sleep.

The nights when the old flower bloomed were rare now. She would wake then slowly in the morning, luxuriously, the plump white arms remembering him who had just quit them. Through the bed-curtains a ray of sunshine found her crumpled cheek, her creased neck amid ringlets, and pointed out her helpless middle age. But, drowsing, Josephine thought she was a girl again, a bride of sixteen. Her half open mouth took on a childish look, a little foolish, more than a little sad.

For that long ago adolescent, "Yeyette" Tascher of Martinique, had gone straight toward heartbreak. A rather fat, badly educated, utterly ignorant and by no means clever child of the tropics, she was shipped off to wintry France, to marry a man who did not want her. Young Alexandre, the Vicomte de Beauharnais, was from the first bored, bored by her. He took her as though it demeaned him; her innocence he made to seem less proper than his conventional corruption. He deserted her for months and years on end, and then slimed her over with accusations about her conduct in his absence. Even for a girl as kindly and as indolent as Yeyette, this husband soon grew insupportable. His own family saw it; they helped her to a separation. So at twenty-two she was the Vicomtesse de Beauharnais, mother of two children, implemented by alimony, beginning to be pretty, with a talent for frivolity and

29

fashion. Thus the Creole blossom parted its white petals.

But on her ignorant head suddenly broke the Revolution. Her affectionate heart took her into the midst of the storm, for Alexandre had been swept up by it and, free of him though she was, Josephine struggled to save him. She pleaded, petitioned, reckless of the danger to herself, until at last she found herself lodged with Alexandre in the Carmelite Nunnery, whose very name was good as sentence to execution.

Josephine screamed and wept; she fainted and went into spasms. It was beyond her to imitate the lofty serenity of the nobles around her awaiting death at the hands of the mob. Day after day she yielded to paroxysms of sheer animal terror till, as her numbered days grew fewer, she became stupefied with fear and, to the relief of all the other prisoners, lay insensible on the floor for hours. Alexandre, too, was at peace; he had lost his head once and for all.

A lady watching at the window of that nunnery prison saw below a woman of the streets who pointed to her dress, her *robe,* and then to a stone, *pierre.* Then she drew a slitting finger across her neck, and laughed and danced on the cobbles. The lady caught her fingers to her lips in comprehension. Robespierre! His head had fallen! The Terror was over. The dazed prisoners were released.

None so dazed as the Widow Beauharnais. She emerged into a world where the aftermath of the Terror was a reign of an equally animal gaiety, a world giddy with folly, fashion, adornment, luxury. Money came from no one knew just where, and flowed on a rising tide of prices into every channel of display. Paris now began to be a woman's town, a town where everyone wanted to know everybody, where nobody wished to be alone for an hour, nor to eat alone or sleep alone. The hot, brilliant, artificial atmosphere was like a forcing house. In it Josephine's thick white petals spread to their full, breathing out their lure.

They had already become just a little brown at the edges, when the young Corsican officer caught the scent and came. He was no match for the languorous Creole charm that she had long learned to practise and to vary with sudden vivacity, a forced girlish enthusiasm that could give way in its turn to the knowledgeable sensuality which the burning young lover called his "miracle."

Now the miracle was something else. Now it was a miracle when from the ashes of her own deceptions that fire ever flared in him again. The drowsing woman writhed a little, prodded by her thoughts, and woke.

Morning sunshine lay calm on the blue satin curtain looped back to the bedpost. Josephine blinked at it, and rolled over on her back. Here was the day, with all its hopes, its agitations, fears, debts, boredom, and itch to get and keep. Uppermost thrust suddenly the panic that so often, these days, showed its ugly head. He had left her so abruptly; was it with surfeit? Had this been the last?

Her mind fled back to the day when she bent to marry him. Yes, actually, she had felt she stooped to an importunate young nobody. But she had kept her head, even as she gave her heart. With worldly foresight she had omitted a religious ceremony. If there was nothing but a civil marriage, she had thought cleverly then, it would be so much the easier to disentangle one's self, should things go badly.

Josephine moaned a little, and sat up. She looked around her at the satin disarray. On the drum-shaped tabouret beside the bed stood empty the wine glass from which last night they had drunk together. A smile tucked up the plump cheeks again. Even the lady-in-waiting attending her in the next room knew what it meant when Josephine entered rubbing her pretty fat little hands together, like a tradesman's wife who has just sold something for twice its worth and plots already where to put her profit.

"Good morning! We have the sun at last, I see. Ah, the yellow roses from Provence!" She deigned to be gracious, even to the huge bouquet, pausing to sniff it; her passion for flowers was perhaps her most sincere. "Today an embroidered muslin," she ordered. "One of those I have not worn. Fetch me new slippers too. A Persian shawl, and my hair to be dressed with *huile antique*."

While her attendant rustled away to the vast armoires housing her regiment of gowns, Josephine sat briskly down to what she called her work table. Like

32

any other craftsman's, it was set with all the tools of her trade, the many little brushes, sticks, puffs, vials, pots, and flasks that went to the making of her *maquillage*, the restoration of her beauty, the daily battle with time. She settled at her table this morning in a mood of victory; she glowed with the consciousness that she had once more dealt age the most defiant blow a woman may give it.

But a glance in her mirror chilled her. Her brows drew quickly together; as quickly she smoothed out the wrinkle, practising a smile to match the blandness of her brow. Noting the effect, she could not help a frown again. That darkening of the teeth. What fools these doctors were who could not cure so grave an ill as that! She tried out a thinner smile, crimping her lips to hide her teeth; it only made her look bitter and defeated.

Unconscious suddenly of her appearance, she sat staring without seeing herself—a woman who had spent everything and got nothing safely hers to keep. A wife who never had been taught her rôle in marriage. The partner of what might have been the greatest enterprise in European history, had she inspired Bonaparte to lift his genius to a higher aim. Time was when he was molten for her hand to shape. Instead she had let slip through her idle, greedy fingers the most phenomenal opportunity for wifehood ever offered. Almost she perceived this, staring blankly at her own frightened face. Then in the glass she saw her attendant enter, heard her speak. Talleyrand was asking audience. Josephine could fairly hear him lick his chops. More trouble! With a sigh of now habitual despair, Josephine turned to her rouge pots for help.

Charles Maurice de Talleyrand-Périgord entered the ornate anteroom next Josephine's dressing-chamber with an air; indeed, he never came into a room in any other way, and there was no room in Europe he would not have known how to perform in. Ex-priest, he still conveyed the intimate profundity of the confessor, as he bowed before the lady and lifted her puffy little hand to his lips like the practised lover of many, which he was.

Josephine's ringed fingers fluttered among the folds of her low-cut bodice; she knew he saw how unevenly it rose and fell. What was he here for? Divorce or debts?

"I have, on your behalf," she heard him saying, "ventured to discuss affairs with Monsieur Bourrienne."

A sigh of arch woe masked her deep relief. Then it was only about bills he came to chivy her! She raised to him those blue eyes that were her Irish heritage, making them swim with pleading tears.

Years ago Josephine had learned how to live on one's debts. She had discovered that his credit is longest who spends most ostentatiously. Even in the days when the young Corsican officer was only a caller at the house in the rue Chanteraine, impressed by its chef and lady's maid, its gardener and its coachman for the black Hungarian horses, the mistress of all that was technically penniless. Already then she had become an expert beseecher and flatterer; she could borrow sum upon sum from bankers with no security except the facile witchery of her smile.

Once she was embarked beside Napoleon on his headlong gambler's career, her bills went soaring. This morning's interview with Talleyrand was not the first of the sort. At one time she had admitted to debts of a million two hundred thousand francs. Bourrienne, the Consul's secretary, in his office tossed her bills up in a blizzard of exasperation. How in the good God's name could any woman want thirty-eight hats in one month? Or wear more than five hundred pairs of shoes a year? Gloves—nearly a thousand pairs of them! For one single shawl, ten thousand francs! As for her jewels, even the crafty appraiser, who gave them less than a third of their actual worth, set his evaluation over four million. She bought any trinket shown her, like a child snatching at a sweet, and either stuffed it forgotten in a drawer, gave it away indifferently, or had it melted down to something else she valued just as little. Her anterooms were always crowded with merchants proffering goods to the greedy fat little hands, the lonely, sterile heart that nursed a lust for objects because it had nothing in it of any real value at all. Potraits, busts, necklaces, lockets, furniture, silks, exotic plants for the hothouse at Malmaison, gowns and more gowns, an artificial orange tree, a monkey that could play the violin—twenty-five million good round francs' worth of such nonsense, in half a dozen years! Was ever there extravagance so thoughtless?

Yes, Napoleon's own. Let him bluster and forgive, and bluster again; Josephine's spending is trivial beside the wastrel act that signed away more than one third of a virgin continent, sight unseen.

For gold that would go up in gunpowder, Napoleon sold, at about four cents an acre, an empire three times the size of France. He sold all the oil fields of Oklahoma, tall Arkansas cypress and black bottom cotton soil, white pine forests of Minnesota, Iowa corn fields, Dakota wheat lands, cattle ranges of Wyoming, Montana copper, Colorado silver and gold, Louisiana rice and sugar. He sold the second greatest river system in the world, from its source to its mouth, and the ocean port thereto appertaining. He, who called himself a founder of empire, sold off the land that could, within fifty years, have fed all the armies of Europe, sated its timber hunger, relieved its population pressure. He sold the sod, blooming with coarse splendid flowers, where forty million bison trampled. The elk, the deer, the beaver and bear, the mink and badger and marten—they all went into the bargain. The southern pines crackling with resin, with precious naval stores of pitch, tar, turpentine, the firs and spruces straight and tall enough to make masts for more ships than ever sailed the seas—these too belonged to Bonaparte. The richest part of the western hemisphere lay in the hollow of his hand.

He did not need to pay a sou or strike a blow to possess it. He had only to keep it.

But grandly he cried to Marbois, his Minister of Finance, "I renounce Louisiana." And for what? To prosecute a war born only of his insane ambition, his inability to keep the peace, his lust for Malta, for Egypt, for India. For fruits long overripe, or sucked dry by former conquest; for dusty memories, for spheres of influence already crowded with immemorial spawning. For these Napoleon renounced Pike's Peak and the Big Horns. He renounced the Nebraska sky arching like a bent bow from horizon to horizon, and the Kansas wind, the Dakota snows. Say of them what you like, they were the making of the men that came to them. He waved away the territories of the Teton Sioux and the fighting Comanches, the fierce Blackfeet and the stately Mandans. Call them our enemies; we are proud of them. The plains, the vast uptilting land spilling its slow rivers eastward, the chain of the Rockies glittering with ice caps—they passed from his hands, and from his people passed the riches that might have been their own.

Thomas Jefferson, president over less than half the states that make our union now, could not yet tabulate this wealth still buried west of the Mississippi. But he looked toward it; he faced the times to come. While Bonaparte had not curiosity enough to wonder what was in that parcel of wilderness he plumped upon the counter, Jefferson was making plans to discover its contents in detail, long before the Purchase was concluded.

A hearth fire in the office kept off the chill of early winter in the marshy new capital. It warmed the sole of Jefferson's old slipper as, one knee crossed over the other, he flexed his foot speculatively up and down from the ankle. He held a paper, written over in his secretary's scholarly hand, and while Lewis waited by his chair in a military "at ease," his chief sat studying this in silence. Across the top ran the heading: *"Recapitulation of an Estimate of the sum necessary to carry into effect the Missie Expedicion."*

"Mathematical Instruments, $217;" read Jefferson. *"Arms and Accoutrements extraordinary, $81; Camp Ecquipage, $255; Medicine & packing, $55; Means of transportation, $430; Indian presents, $696—"*

Smiling, he looked up over the glasses his keen eyes needed only for reading. "You calculate to a nicety, young man," he murmured.

"The money I must spend is the nation's," replied Lewis gravely.

Jefferson settled his spectacles and went back to his perusal of the list.

"Provisions extraordinary, $224; Materials for making up the various articles into portable packs, $55; For the pay of hunters, guides, and interpreters, $300; In silver coin, to defray the expences of the party from Nashville to the last white settlement on the Missisourie, $100; Contingencies, $87—"

He laid the paper on his knee. " 'Contingencies,' " he quoted slowly, and sat for a long minute looking into the flames. His heart, full of a youthful appetite for adventure which made him envy the man at his side, was nevertheless deeply troubled. Meriwether Lewis he loved like the son he did not have. The boy to him was his spearhead into the future, almost as though he had begotten him. Now his own hand would launch that spear upon a course so dangerous no man could count its dangers. Lewis himself listed them all under one laconic word. *Contingencies*. The fire danced before the older man's spectacled gaze like flames round an Indian stake.

"I think," said the low voice quietly at his side, "that covers everything, sir."

"Ah, yes!" The President picked up the sheet again. "At eighty-seven dollars, eh? You're counting on luck, I see. And the total?" He lifted the paper a little closer. "Two thousand five hundred dollars," he read aloud.

That is the sum, as it stands in the books today. That is the appropriation requested of Congress to finance the boldest and the most fruitful exploration that history records. Columbus, if you like, found a new hemisphere. But that was done by luck; it was in fact a mischance, for the old eastern dream blinded even his eyes. La Salle, De Soto, Ponce de Leon, they went, but did they get back again? Coronado left no more than a trail of blood to mark his futile search for gold through Kansas grasses. Lewis and Clark went forth, not to conquer, only to find the way in which a peaceful nation might march, by home and farm, by mill and mine, to the western sea that Nature set it for a boundary.

ᘇᕓ IV

THE VILLAGE CAPITAL of the United States lay somnolent amid its fields, its tulip trees and chestnut oaks, upon the third of July, 1803. In the embassies ran rumor, contemptuous but troubled. Mr. Merry of England was sour. Yrujo, that grandee of Spain, thought he knew all, and so said little. Turreau of France flicked at his gaudy uniform, with the confidence of the minister of a nation which owned more of America than the Americans did. The ambassador of Catherine the Great was uneasy, like a cat that dreads to be disturbed. As July the third grew older, rumor turned to news that swept the embassies like the rising of a storm at the end of a long hot day. Louisiana was sold by Napoleon to the United States!

The young giant feared by all of Europe's powers had grown suddenly double in size. Yrujo's breast heaved under its frills; by the treaty of San Ildefonso, he scolded, Napoleon had not the right to sell, and Jefferson had no right to buy stolen goods! The Czarina's ambassador arched his back; in one stride the giant had come more than a thousand miles closer to Russian

America. Turreau stood dumbfounded, and Merry hastened off to whisper with the Federalists, whose hate of Jefferson he forever abetted.

From the foreign ministers to their aides, from the cabinet members to their families, from the congressmen to their ladies in the boarding-houses, from the boarding-house servants to the urchins in the street, the news sped like a ball down hill. Without a shot, we had bested Napoleon. We had thrust ourselves boldly forth, our back heaving strong under Canada; we had thrown ourselves upon the Spanish Southwest; our hands were reaching toward the Pacific. We were free with a new and spacious grandeur.

Washington, the common man's Washington, comes to life in summer after sundown. The fireflies thread the streets, their greeny-gold lanterns bobbing. In the woods, exhaling a first coolness, the whippoorwills call, without a breath between; the mosquitoes hum at the netting, and in the dusky alleys there is black laughter and the yodel of children signaling to one another over back fences. That night, when great news leaped from mouth to mouth like laughter, the boys in the streets began to light their firecrackers. The nation, in its rejoicing, could not wait till morning to celebrate its twenty-seventh birthday.

The Fourth of July began with thrush song, some of the last of the year perhaps, before that tender voice would fall silent, abashed by brazen heat. Then the southern catbird, declaiming bird oratory, then the blood-red cardinal shouting his "Three cheers! Three cheers!" A spluttering of crackers ran like a little ground fire through the Washington streets. Sleepers turned, and stretched, and looked toward the sky. Then from the Potomac shore a salvo of cannon shook the town.

Boom! A shot, let's say, in honor of our new port, New Orleans. There was a furious barking of dogs. People sat up in bed, ran to the windows, hurried, if they were dressed, into the streets.

Boom! A shot for bold St. Louis with its three streets. The listeners looked in each other's eyes and smiled. Yes, this was it. This was the lean old man with the white eyebrows and the spunky goatee, telling the world.

Boom! One for you, Long Tom, Mr. President in your carpet slippers, quizzically smiling, head thrust a little forward the better to see a century hence. *Boom!* That's for Mississippi, for the men of the western waters, for Kentucky with its rifles cocked, and coonskin Tennessee. *Boom!* Salute to you, Mr. Monroe, far away over the sea in Paris. *Boom!* And to you, Mr. Gallatin, you who keep the treasury so well that fifteen million dollars is not too much to pay for a pig in a poke. *Boom!* for the newest star in the flag, Ohio. *Boom!* What's that for? Did a little boy shout, "For buffaloes"? Then here's to the buffaloes! *Boom!* for the Indians. *Boom!* for the Stony Mountains with their heads wrapped in swirling snow, their thunderstorms and lightning bolts, their glaciers flashing signals from their summits. *Boom!* for the Union, may it stand forever! *Boom!* for the Constitution. *Boom!* for the prairies, and the states there yet unborn—razor-backed Missouri, sunflower Kansas, the rippling Dakotas, old lady Iowa with the lilacs sprigged on her Sunday gown. *Boom!* Each blast shook the air, rattled the windows, had not died away over the hills when came another—*Boom!* Won't they go roaring drunk in the taverns tonight? What'll they say in New York? In Philadelphia? In Boston? *Boom!* for the states to be hewn from the Rockies, Montana of the chinooks, Colorado with breasts of snow and dark coniferous skirts, Wyoming with its lariat swinging. *Boom!* The sky at last was silent, and the earth shook now no more.

To the White House flowed a stream, ceaseless, jubilant, tramping, mincing, chattering, all coming to shake the President's hand. Punch filled the great bowls and ebbed out of them; ales, wines and brandies were uncorked and emptied, for every glass went high in a toast to the day. South Carolina congratulates you, Mr. President. The Senate congratulates you. The House of Representatives congratulates you. Kentucky thanks you. The Supreme Court is worried, Mr. President. The Federalist boarding-houses can't afford not to join in the crush. They congratulate you, and it gripes, Mr. President, it gripes them to the liver. Tennessee thanks you. The territory of Maine thanks you. Virginia is proud of her son, statesman, scholar, philosopher, liberal—not least of all with his punch.

44

So the green comber of national triumph descended on the Federalist party, singing in their ears. What members came up sputtering had had all specious love of the West washed out of them. "You have no authority," Quincy told Congress, shaking a long finger, "to throw the rights and property of this people into the *hotch-potch* with the wild men on the Missouri. . . . Do you suppose the people of the Northern and Atlantic States will, or ought to, look on with patience and see Representatives and Senators from the Red River and Missouri pouring themselves upon this and the other floor, managing the concerns of a seaboard fifteen hundred miles, at least, from their residence?"

We are sorry to alarm the Gentleman from Massachusetts, but that sounds quite a bit like the thing that is going to happen. Yes, just that might come to pass. The Gentleman from South Dakota has the floor. The Gentleman from Idaho asks leave to put a question. The Gentleman from Washington proposes a dam at the Grand Coulee . . . That roaring flood which swamped the little men from the little states was the tide of great events. It was not to be stayed by cries of "Unconstitutional!"

True that the frame of government held no warrant for Thomas Jefferson's bold act. Strict constructionist that he was, he afterward suggested that an amendment might be needed. The people said, "Forget it." They said, "You did all right." In an overwhelming vote the Purchase was ratified by Congress, and the people nodded. "We're watching out for the Constitution," they told their President. "Go on, Long Tom, until we stop you. Go on and lead us."

So trusted, worthy of such trust, Jefferson stood taller than all the men of stature about him and looking westward saw how far, indeed, he must lead the nation. The lands all the way to the Rockies were now assured by purchase, but from the Rockies to the Pacific Ocean must lie vast terrain, he perceived, that as yet belonged to no government upon earth. Soon enough would claims be pressed upon it. From Alta California, where the bells were calling in the lonely missions, Spain could stretch up a hand to lay upon that unexplored region. From Alaska, Russia might reach down a paw. Already England's rights were well established north of the mighty westward river. But it had been America's own Captain Gray who, from the sea, had found its mouth, and named it for his ship, Columbia. Thus had been staked our claim at an outpost farthest west. What Jefferson saw was that he must send the flag straight through the Rockies and down the Columbia to the sea, and so forestall all alien powers and make this unknown soil of America forever American.

With his own blend of prudence and audacity, he had long since laid all his plans for this. Now broke the morning of their execution.

The fifth day of July in this country of ours is apt to be washed by a mood of sober reaction from excess of high spirits. It begins with a quietude the deeper for yesterday's detonations. The air is the cleaner for a dawn breeze that sweeps the last sulphurous taint of fireworks out of the sky. The glorious boasts are done with, for this year; now the citizenry must set about its various tasks of execution.

On the short night between the fourth and fifth of July, 1803, Meriwether Lewis was again sleeping under the President's roof, a transient visitor in the house that for nearly two years had been his home. Here the young soldier had been silent witness at the inner councils of the nation. At secret cabinet meetings his was the pen that took rapid notes of the casual, witty, philosophic utterances of the President, of little Mr. Madison's fiery rejoinders, Mr. Monroe's judicious qualifications, the Swiss-accented observations of Mr. Gallatin. Here he had been not only personal but social secretary to the widowed Chief Executive, deft among the influential ladies, the ambassadors, the potent senators. Here he had sat over nuts and wine after those four-o'clock dinners provided by the personally simple and lavishly hospitable Jefferson, while Tom Paine, slouching ill-kempt in his chair, rolled out long periods like a sequel to his *Rights of Man*. From here young Lewis had set forth, in days now gone, to ride the dogwood-covered hills of Virginia alone with Theodosia Burr, sending rumors to fly through the boarding-houses. "And she so lately the wife of an Allston of South Carolina, my dear!"

Now all that was over, and forever. These few last days in Washington had been but an interlude in which

47

Lewis felt himself already a stranger to this life of polish and diplomacy. Since April he had been away on special leave of absence, to prepare for the unfathomable experience ahead. He had been to Lancaster, to learn astronomy and the use of its instruments from Mr. Andrew Ellicott, and to Philadelphia to study natural history under Dr. Wistar and Dr. Barton. From boyhood Lewis had had an eye and a mind for the Nature of his native South, so that his studies had but perfected an ability to note the new and classify it. He had been, too, to Harper's Ferry to oversee the manufacture of rifles and of tomahawks, and the building of his boat *Experiment*.

And so back to Washington, and a few more nights of this soft bed, this quiet chamber. Every preparation now was made; all that was foreseeable had been provided for, the arms and pirogues ordered, the instruments selected for survey and navigation, the medals for the Indian chiefs struck, the wampum and trading stock laid in, the flags sewn, the medicines made up, the camping gear packed, with clothing for many months and many weathers—all the items had been thought of, bought, made, which today fill fifteen pages of finely printed inventory. So Lewis was ready to steer his course by the stars, over the frozen waves of a continent tossed up in stone two miles high.

In these last days of crisis, crowded with the tension and the triumph of Louisiana purchased, the President had nevertheless found time for the most careful check with Lewis of every preparation.

"After all," he remarked, with a private smile between them, "we two have been comrades in this alone together for a long time. I should like to see it through with you as far as I may go."

He did not speak of the list of the brave men or the clever men, the cautious and the adventurous who had all failed in what was now to be attempted. It had been the dream of Nicolet, of Rogers the Ranger, of the Verendryes. In 1794 Jean Baptiste Trudeau was firmly resolved to follow the headwater of the Missouri to reach the Pacific; he succeeded only in attaining the Mandan villages of Dakota. Next came Lecuyer, who managed so badly that he never got past the Ponca Indians. Scotchman Mackay fared no better than those before him. Welshman Evans, carrying the flag of Spain, obsessed by the myth of Welsh Indians in the interior, was stopped too at the Mandan villages.

Over Vancouver's map of the Oregon coast, one of Captain Gray's showing the mouth of the Columbia, and other less reliable charts of the interior, the President pored long, with Lewis at his elbow. The gnarled finger followed the crooked courses, accurate and inaccurate, real and imaginary, of these fragmentary evidences, and came again to pause before the great blank, the unknown, the wall of the Rockies.

"It is there," Jefferson murmured, "that the crux lies.

There must be a one right pass from the true and farthest headwaters of the Missouri, that should bring you down upon the sources of the Columbia."

Lewis leaned forward on his knuckles, his young hands that would carve the way lying close to the old ones that first had pointed it.

"More easily than not," pursued the President, "one could there go astray and, all unknown, come down on the headwaters of the Rio Bravo, and so only back to Texas. Just as easily," he argued with enjoyment, judiciously settling his spectacles, "one might strike the drainage of the Colorado, which would unfortunately lead down to the Gulf of California. And so again you fall into the hands of Spain. They must, these rivers, all head up somewhat in the same territory."

"And our choice of them must be at once the right one," Lewis said. "We must drive straight through, sir, at one trial. Time and supplies permit of no error."

"You will make none," the older man promised him. He clapped him gently on the shoulder. "You will get through and reach the coast of the Pacific. From there it might be well for some of the party—all, if you so find it advisable, to return by sea, either by the Horn or the Cape of Good Hope. You will be then without money or provisions. So I have here prepared"—he groped in a drawer for a certain paper—"a letter of credit for you." He found it and gave it into the younger man's hand.

The State Department still preserves that half-sheet

pledging the credit of a nation to—what? Indian chiefs who value a blue bead above all else, rivers that run reckless of the gold in them, the cold peaks and the hot winds and the vast indifferent spaces. But Jefferson's far sight probed every possible necessity with a zest to forestall it. Over the many pages of official instructions to Lewis he had in the past weeks spent loving hours. A cipher had been worked out for communication between them, the key-word being "artichokes." All Jefferson's boyish inventiveness, all his ardor for discovery, his scientific interest in birds and plants and weather observations, found vent in the expedition that he might not join, and the past few days of preparation with young Lewis had filled him with a grave exhilaration.

Now the morning of departure had come. Before this fifth day of July had seen the sun, Lewis arose and in the half light made his soldierly toilette. To shave, he had need to light a candle; the little oval of glass, as he dried his face, gave him back a last reflection of the private secretary, smooth, scholarly, with the healthy pallor of a man who need not go abroad in extreme weathers. The looking-glass would never see this face again. But there was none of the mirror-gazer in Meriwether Lewis. He looked inward, by temperament; his friend Jefferson spoke afterward of the depressions that in these White House years shadowed the younger man.

The dawn was lightening now. Once dressed, Lewis strapped up his remaining personal luggage with his own hands, out of a poor opinion of the negroes' knots. In a few minutes one of the blacks would come to carry his baggage to be driven to the Harper's Ferry stage. And so by Charleston, Frankfort, Uniontown and Redstone Old Fort to Pittsburg.

The humble knuckles of the negro servant sounded just then on the door. Lewis opened to him and bade him take the ready baggage. He picked up his hat, tucked it beneath his arm and walked softly down the corridor of the sleeping mansion to say his farewell. A line of light from under Jefferson's door greeted him. He tapped, and at the cordial answer entered.

The strapping young black detailed to wait on Lewis, having piled the baggage ready in the coach, returned for any further orders. The secretary's room was empty; Cato guessed where he must be. He idled in the corridor waiting. Here, outside an open window, a rising wind of morning plowed the dark tree-tops. Presently Cato could make out the pattern of the hall carpet. So he stepped down the hall to snuff out a night lamp burning there, and heard from deeper in the house the snick of a door opening and closing, then the step of Mr. Lewis coming, in its quick fall a sound of departure and of enterprise.

The problem that faced Meriwether Lewis, as he journeyed the second week in July across the Alleghenies, was the same that had met all those who went before him, and thrown them back, defeated.

The first steps west were easiest. Provided you could fight, sneak, or buy your way past the Osages and Omahas, the Arikaras, Kiowas and Poncas that lined the banks of the lower Missouri, it was not too difficult to reach the Mandan villages. Already white men were familiar there, who made this their westernmost outpost of trade. But only one party, the Verendryes, had ever got beyond the earthen lodges on the steep river bluffs.

For they held a strategic position, these long-haired, proud, pale Mandans. Their villages, and those of the Minnetarees across the river, were built near the great bend of the Missouri. There the upstream traveler no longer found the highway taking him north; there the course turns westward, toward the Rockies.

So the Mandans held the gateway to the Rocky Mountain fur trade, and they had come to understand this. They knew that if white traders should push beyond them and begin trading powder, whisky, tobacco, pots, pans, cottons, beads and axes directly with the mountain tribes, in exchange for furs, then they, the Mandans, would no longer as middlemen have the best of the bargain both ways. Well they understood the art of detaining a traveler till his articles of barter were all consumed in buying food, or were filched, bit by bit, or demanded as bribes of state.

All this Lewis knew, and looked past, to a farther obstacle. He foresaw that the day must come, somewhere at the foot of the Rockies near the Missouri's distant source, when his boats could no longer navigate that dwindling stream. There they must be abandoned, and from that point he must portage his baggage—the bales of trading stock which was to be his medium of exchange from tribe to tribe, the powder and lead and guns that in peace meant sustenance and in war safety, as well as the food, instruments and records. An unknown distance must all this be carried, across mountains of unknown height and declivity, before a waterway to the Pacific could be discovered. There fresh boats must be built, out of suitable timber to be found and felled. And for the whole length of that portage, and continuously while the boats were buried and other boats built, while the baggage was repacked for carriage and toilsomely moved, the expedition, its lives and goods, would be at the mercy of the Indians.

Of these, there was one tribe that, like the Mandans, guarded a gate in the way. This was the pass through the Rockies, the door that Lewis must first find, then open and enter. This far had the Verendryes come, some half century earlier, this far and no farther. For they had had no key to the door.

The tribe who dwelt in that pass, Lewis knew, were of the Shoshone people. And he knew that they, alone among their neighbors, were mounted. Word of the Shoshone horses had blown across the plains, even to the frontier of the white man's world. Lewis had heard it. He knew, moreover, that these horses were to him a vital necessity. He must have them, to make that portage over the mountains with his goods. He must somehow obtain them of their warlike riders at the very threshold of the door in the mountains. He could not force that door; he must not fight this crucial tribe. Approaching them in boats, he foresaw, he would encounter them at the very point where the boats must be abandoned. He must go forward afoot, in an attitude almost of petition, to meet those fierce knights of the plain and mountain.

To win the Shoshones over, and open the door in the Rockies, was the great problem. Failing in this, all their courage and perseverance had availed nothing to the Verendryes. They came to the Rockies with Mandan guides, but Shoshones did not trust Mandans, and the guides themselves neither trusted nor cared about the Frenchmen. They quailed before their own stories of the terrors of the mountain tribes; they melted away. At the gates of the Rockies the Verendryes were left speechless, without guides, before a hostile people. They turned back, their dream of the western waters forever unslaked.

Over and over were white men thus betrayed by the red men whose empire they dared to enter. It was an Indian who tried to lure Coronado to his death, leading him on across the plains of Kansas and Nebraska, in search of a mythical Grand Quivira where the poorest man ate from dishes of gold. True that Lewis was asking his way not to gold but to the Pacific. But an Indian tells you the lies you ask for.

What key, then, will open for Meriwether Lewis the door in the mountains? It must be of nothing less than gold, of the truest metal. And it must be curiously shaped, for the lock is an intricate one. To fit it, find then an Indian without alloy of Indian deceit, venality, cowardice. One who not only speaks the tongue of the Shoshones, but knows and is known to them. Who can find them if they hide, and who, if they ride forth to fight, can pacify them. A Shoshone, in short, but it must be a Shoshone of that very tribe, the Lemhi tribe inhabiting the pass.

And it must be one—if such an Indian can be imagined—who can not be bought nor bribed, who will not suddenly quit the party altogether, to chase buffalo or a girl. An Indian who will not demand his pay in advance, get drunk, and disappear. One whose loyalty runs deeper and binds tighter than mere advantage. Centuries before, one such brightened a bloody page of history; had Lewis paused over it, some quiet evening in Jefferson's long study? There he could read how essential to the success of Cortez had been his interpreter, Mariana, the Aztec captive who became the captain's mistress.

Now when a man acts, he acts either for his own interests or in loyalty to some cause—tribe, guild, country, army, or religion. But a simple woman seldom has any genuine attachment to a cause. It is a man she follows, and she espouses whatever cause he upholds. Into it she need not deeply inquire, nor sound its worthiness. It is the man who must to her be worth devotion; then his cause is good enough for her. In serving it, she serves him; this is her single purpose; this is her strength. For him she will walk barefoot on thorns, and carry great weights upon her back.

So the gold must be beaten into a woman's shape, to fit the lock. In the Mandan villages, at the great bend of the Missouri, was the key, ready to the courageous hand.

❧ V

WITH A COMMOTION like a black ant nest's, the slave quarters of Mulberry Hill mustered out to say goodbye to York. York was so black he had blue highlights on his cheekbones; he was gigantesque—one of the Ashantis, perhaps; he stood a little taller than his tall master, William Clark, and his pate was as fiercely frizzled as Clark's was fiery red.

His fellow slaves goggled with excitement; the women's high-pitched laughter shrilled nervously until the hens took it up in hysterical imitation. The black children wailed, strutted, hid, or sucked their thumbs and widened their eyes, according to temperament. "Lose yo' scalp suah!" the other bucks told him. "How you gwine get on 'thouten Doll?" "Or Liz and Rosy?" Everybody hooted at this, and York laughed ruefully; he didn't know how.

The talk swirled back to the Indian dangers, subject to which all black conversation had been gravitating for a week, ever since Mister Lewis wrote Master William from Cincinnati he was acomin' suah fo' to fetch him, and Master William had promised York to take him along. The laughter, rumbling or rising, hid envy of York and real fear for him. Even here in Louisville, now fortified by a thousand souls all told, the Indian wars of Boone and Wayne were still acrid on the air, like a whiff of gunpowder knocked out of an old horn.

But the wide low nostrils of big York scented hungrily the adventure on the air, as the stags at this season were flairing their does. For it was October now; that's Indian summer in Kentucky, when the hardwoods put on their warpaint, and violet mists curl on the Ohio, till even near hills are dreamy with imagined distance. When the hickorynuts and butternuts come rattling down like shot upon the cabin roofs, as the night wind racks the branches, and the pigeons turn south. Lewis had seen them, as he came down the Ohio, passing overhead like a whistling cloud. He had noted that the black squirrels were "driving," making a pellmell exodus southwest, swimming the river agile as rats, jumping with autumn tingle through the trees.

Here at the Falls of the Ohio, men too were gathering for departure. Those Clark had chosen were all out of Kentucky, that Indian border that like a blooded steel whetted a man's edge. They were all young, so young there was no holding them. They were all limber-tough, seasoned from birth, suckled on the wolf milk of wilderness. They were a southern kind of man, with voices soft to conceal a deadly courage, with hands so idle at rest you wouldn't think how quick they'd be to kill. Clark, knowing this breed by heart, had spotted them out throughout the state, picking them from the many. Not for nothing had he fought at Fallen Timbers and seen service from the Western Reserve to the Natchez Trace. There was no horse he could not ride, and no mark he could not hit, and men like his recruits would have been proud to follow him to hell and back.

So here they were ready. John Shields, good shot, good waterman, knew guns as a surgeon knows vitals; coals, bellows and iron he could handle as well as wood. William Bratton was a gunsmith too, and ingenious with his hands. Nathaniel Pryor had a steady head, to match his shooting finger. The two Fields boys, Reuben and Joseph, quick as wildcats, sharp as hawks, asked only to be first in every danger. John Colter longed to see the last of chimney smoke forever. Alexander Willard, Joseph Whitehouse, William Werner and brave Charles Floyd cradled their guns with the same look in their eyes. A look that is sometimes a glaze, like a bird's, and then again a light, like sundown burning gold in a high window far away. You may have seen it, fading, in the eyes of certain last old men—the look that means West.

On a fall day warm as a fed animal's breath, Clark led these men, York bringing up the rear, to Louisville wharf where lay the iron boat *Experiment*. The apple of Lewis's eye, it had been built to his specifications, and named with a well-founded misgiving. Louisville opined it was the quarest broadhorn ever they did see, and Clark as he came aboard laughed out of the warmth of his lungs, the way he had, letting the laughter out like a glad hound barking and bounding. But though you could never tell whether he laughed at you or with you or to something behind your shoulder, you could count on his kindness.

The hand of Lewis tingled with pleasure as it left Clark's. The bigger man gripped him lightly by the shoulder. "By God!" he said. "By God!" And he laughed again so that Lewis laughed, and the bladelike light of grinning flashed across all the faces.

"Captain Clark," said Lewis, in a voice lifted for the ears of those others, "if you had not agreed to share with me the first command of this expedition, I could not have consented to accept from the President the under-taking of a journey to the Pacific."

"If you hadn't asked me," said Clark, "I and some of these boys would have been laying for you in the Rocky Mountains." And he worried genially the big muzzle pushed into his hand, Scannon, the Newfoundland, lean-ing all his weight in sudden fondness against him. Dogs, babies, Indians, children and women, as well as gentle-men and soldiers, loved Billy Clark at sight.

"Where did you get this recruit?" he asked now, as Scannon lunged to plant both forepaws on his chest.

"I bought him in Pittsburg; an Indian has already of-fered me double his price, but there was no bargain, was there, Scannon?" Lewis smiled.

"Signed up for the full journey, has he?"

"Without reservation," answered Lewis, calling the beast off Clark with a snap of fingers. "The other recruits are still on trial," he added, lifting his voice again. "You must meet the men I've picked, Captain Clark."

The Kentucky men looked over the Pittsburg lot with wary eyes, as they greeted them. Most that Lewis had chosen were men of the regular army.

"Of Potts and Collins and Wiser I'm pretty sure," Lewis said, standing apart with Clark. "Hugh McNeal may be overlively, but I think him sound. This young George Shannon pleased me on the instant."

"The lad with the black hair and blue eyes? He looks a gentleman." Clark called to him to come. "Where are you from, son?" he inquired kindly.

Graceful, gay, easy with breeding, and sparkling with Irish response, Shannon stood looking his captains straight. "From Belmont County, sir, in Ohio."

"Shannon?" said Clark, tasting it for remembrance. "I think I know of the Shannons, don't I?"

"We would hope you might, Captain Clark," George answered neatly.

But Shannon did not help his captains out, with any family reminiscence. If they placed his father, who had been prominent, or the Jane Milligan who was his mother, the captains might communicate with her; that redoubtable woman was not a river mile too safely distant, even now. A little inquiry right here would have turned up the fact that George was a runaway from school, only sixteen years old. Well built, well grown, he looked the man, and Lewis had accepted him as such. But the truth of it was that when George encountered

62

Lewis, on the way to Pittsburg, the academy there was just taking up its fall term, with the name of George Shannon on the roster. The less said about himself the better, George had concluded.

So, in a boy's dream of high adventure come true, they floated down the river. They picked up men to complete the party on their way, some, you'd say, out of the woods and off the river, some from the forts at Vincennes and Kaskaskia. Volunteers pushing out of the army ranks passed before the scrutiny of Lewis in their officers' quarters; he looked them over, as a woodsman looks over timber out of which he will build a ship. Man after man, tens, dozens, scores and hundreds all told, stood for him to measure, and when he saw a pair of shoulders broad enough and eyes that gave him the look he wanted, he nodded, and the man was told to strip to the waist. Then from each body there came a brief glow into the winter chill of the room, of animal warmth and strength, and as the doctor bent to listen to the heart's beat and the song of the lungs, Lewis looked closely. You can tell a man who has worked with his body from childhood by the deep quilting of muscles over the shoulders and the twist of them like hornbeam stems in the arms. You can know, by the vertical narrow navel, a man who can lift a log out of the way and a boat off a sandbar. But the eyes tell most. And one of a hundred would give his eyes to Lewis, across the doctor's head, and silently take his oath.

Thompson, Frazier and George Gibson were of these,

63

and so were the three Massachusetts men, Goodrich and Howard and Hall. Ordway was a Yankee too, from Captain Bissell's company at Kaskaskia, with the granite look around the mouth of fine old New Hampshire stock. Bissell fought to keep back the Irishman Gass, too good a carpenter to let go, and too old, so he argued with Lewis—all of thirty-two. The hot Irish eyes pleaded; and studying the short, broad-chested, wiry body, Lewis smiled a promise.

Out of the woods came Drouillard, George Drouillard, begot by some Canadian Frenchman on an Indian squaw. She gave him his tracker's cunning, his glibness with sign language, his perdurable vitality. He shot like a god who could not miss; he could run like the wind; woods and prairie were natural to him as to an animal. Peter Cruzatte was a man of the river; for all his one blind eye, he could read water like a book. He asked one thing: might he bring his fiddle? And Clark, once he heard him play, clapped his shoulder and warned him never to drop it.

So they went into winter quarters on the little flood plain of Wood Creek in Illinois. It comes in, a modest river out of a peaceful state, to join the Mississippi nearly opposite the junction of that stream with its elder brother the Missouri, that was their road into wilderness. The woods stood naked then, the leaves going to mould, and frost penciling twigs and canes. There was good game all round about, turkey and deer, from here to

Lake Michigan, and settlers so few and far apart their woodsmoke was a rare thin loneliness against the sky.

Here the winter was passed in drilling the men, building boats, practising with fire-arms, and creating the spirit that would take them through, from there and back. Call it, if you must, morale, *esprit de corps*; we know it, anyway, as the thing that got the Continental army through Valley Forge, pulled Texas, lusty and bawling, out of the womb of Mexico, did all that we have ever done together, to make us great. Perhaps we shall find some good plain American word to name it by, when every man among us has it in him.

Bloodroot was white in the woods, and the shad were running, when they got ready to break camp. On the ninth of May, at St. Louis, they stood at attention—a little body of men hewn like the flint tip of an arrow that now was notched in the string. This was the last Spanish post in Louisiana, and only now had the slow and cumbersome deference of nations come to the point of its surrender. So Major Amos Stoddard had crossed from Cahokia in Illinois, to stand ready. The soft spring air was solemn, yet jubilant. Slowly the flag of Spain crumpled upon its standard, then rushed in a cloud of gold and scarlet forever from that sky. The flag of France was run up, flapped once in surprising incarnation on the May breeze and fell again, to die in a soldier's hand. Then, while the men of Lewis and Clark stood at salute, Major Stoddard ordered his colors up, to float as long as the wind shall blow here.

Five days later the bow was stretched, the arrow sped. The prows of the expedition were set up into the freshet flood of the dark Missouri.

ᕓ VI

THE MISSOURI, to the men who have to travel by it, is not merely a river but a calamity. It carries three times as much silt as the Nile; it is the dirtiest river in the world, and the most changeable, with a treacherous shift to it like that in the tail of a plotting big cat. If you could straighten out its kinks, it would be long enough to stretch from Lake Erie to the Pacific Ocean. And there is fight in those kinks; they are strewn with sandbars, visible and invisible, snags, sawyers, and floating booms that are whole pieces of island.

So Clark and Lewis took five and a half months to go from the mouth of the Missouri to the Great Bend in what is now North Dakota. Theirs were the largest boats that had ever ascended this stream, and thus theirs was the most difficult and tedious navigation. There were constant halts to supply the expedition with game, and others to call a council with the tribes and chiefs along the banks. Everywhere the red man must be told that neither Spain nor France now claimed this territory, and that their Great White Father now lived in Washington city; the serene profile of Mr. Jefferson, struck off on medals for this purpose, passed from one curious copper palm to another. The blue American army coats and cocked hats were donned by pleased chiefs over their painted nakedness, the pipes were smoked, the answering speeches made. Then next morning the boats must be shoved off again, and pushed on up against the current.

Through those months the personnel was tested and tempered by first hardships. One man, Charles Floyd, an excellent sergeant, died of sudden illness, and Pat Gass by popular vote was elected in his place. Two men deserted, one was lost, and one talked mutiny and was cast out. French watermen came on, as they were needed, and were dropped off again along the river.

Now at last, in the Mandans' moon of falling leaves, our late October, the white men are coming to the first great gate across their route. There will be many other barriers; they will be mountains and rapids and hunger and Indian suspicion. This gate at the Great Bend is soon to be locked by winter; here they must wait till spring swings it open. High overhead the geese and brant were streaking southward; each morning the northern sun rose later and breath was easier to see. They were all tough men, yet they shivered. But the Teton Sioux hunting along the banks went naked without gooseflesh, and a buffalo robe was enough for a Mandan.

The Mandans were the people among whom Lewis and Clark proposed to wait out the cold months. They were the last Indians, the farthest out upon the grass wilderness, of whom Lewis had been able to obtain any clear information. Men came up from St. Louis and down from Manitoba to trade with them; and stories of their barbaric wealth, their easy and even lavish hospitality, their stately bodies, their almost white skins, their fair-haired women, were rumored all the way to the Atlantic. The Mandans were a fabulous people while they yet lived.

Far below their inhabited villages the explorers came upon the abandoned ruins of their former kingdom, fortified towns upon the bluffs and reaching far over the plain, in the midst of a deep, soft fertility deserted now and turned to autumn. These marked the first footsteps of the Mandans' ultimate departure. Clark and Lewis saw the skulls of this people's ancestors set there in circles, still holding a kind of ghostly council on the sod. But the skulls and ruins only raised the expectations all the young men had, as the buffalo had lifted their hearts by sheer numbers.

Prospecting from the top of some bluff or butte, the leaders and hunters could see, around them in the vast circle of prairie, herds of bison and antelope grazing in a congregate calm that even more than numbers showed their plenty. But start a horseman toward them, and they streamed like the Dakota wind, each antelope a light streak, and every buffalo two thundering tons of sullen meat. All night endured the howl and skulk of everlasting wolf hunger.

Like its animal abundance, the planted crops of this

land were fat. The mucky bottoms were easy to till, even by crude Mandan farming, and now in October the harvest was in, of many-colored hardy corn, many-shaped horny squash, beans, sunflower seed and tobacco. The grain brimmed to the earthen borders of the six-foot sunken caches; the pumpkin hung to dry in strips, with the last of the corn pulled in the milk, from scaffolds before the earthen lodges. They were like hives, these lodges, circular, crowding around a central space where the Mandans played their games and danced their ceremonies.

The boom of the swivel gun from the prow of the *Experiment* brought everyone in the Mandan villages to his feet. News of the approaching pirogues had already flown ahead, but the gun from the thunder-canoe startled all. There were three white men in the villages, who heard it, and they, better than the Indians, understood what it meant that the Yankees had got here at last. One was a visiting trader from the Hudson's Bay Company in Canada, a man who resented the coming intrusion. One was René Jessaume, a French Canadian go-between who had much intelligence and all of it evil. And one was Toussaint Charbonneau.

This was the first white man ever to have seen Saca-jawea. He saw her the night the Knife River Minneta-rees brought her here for sale. She was a small captive animal then, whose black eyes snapped with pride of race and with hatred of the Pah-kes who had driven her here, starved, beaten, kicked, on a forced march of hundreds of miles. She had lost her moccasins long before; her feet were bleeding and swollen with stone cuts and the spines of prickly-pear and barbs of wild grass. Her garments had been wagered away, her braids undone by her captors who, being of the Sioux nation, preferred long flowing hair. This and her fierce pride clothed her handsomely, as she stood in the shadows watching the fire-lit gambling game in which she was the stake.

From his own corner of the lodge, Charbonneau smoked and also watched—the game and the girls. None of it shocked or surprised him; this was the world he was part of. He was one of those men, to be found in the submerged levels of any civilization, who despise "the natives," cheat them, abuse them, and yet cannot live apart from them. Not only do these men fasten themselves upon a simpler people as the shortest way to gain a livelihood, but they are at ease only in their company, and do not disdain to have the despised blood run in the veins of their own children. Charbonneau was happy, in the earthen lodges at the bend of the Missouri. No white men but his own kind ever came this way. His laziness was paid for by his Indian slave women, for every Indian woman expected to slave for her man. His immorality found a respectable vent in the accepted Mandan custom of concubinage. If he was a poor hunter, he was a sharp trader. He was a gambler where it was no vice to gamble, but rather a social accomplishment, and tonight he watched the toss of the sticks with more than usual interest.

For across the fire he saw that the stakes were worth playing for. It was a child he looked at, a naked child, and he thought of her thus, less with lust than with the calculation of a horse-trader. He saw the intelligence, wary and tiptoe, moving behind the dark scorn in her stare. He saw how sturdily the little bronze body was made, and that the face was lovely, undisfigured by the tattooing that made so many Mandan women hideous. Charbonneau at forty knew one thing well, in his slack, rule-of-thumb way, and that was Indians. This Indian, alien, ungrown, contemptibly female, was in time to be assayed by the wise of earth as pure gold. Even Charbonneau caught the glint, that night by the fire; he stepped up indolently and took a part in the game.

Maybe he cheated; it would have been like him; maybe he had luck. At any rate, the Shoshone girl child was at last thrust toward him. He bought another of the stolen Shoshones too, an older girl named Otterwoman who became his wife at once.

By now, in the fall of 1804, Sacajawea was also a wife to him, a slave to bear his pack and soon his child. When the *Experiment*'s gun boomed down the river, she looked at Otterwoman with a light of excitement flaring in her eyes. Otterwoman looked frightened, but Sacajawea got up quickly, ran to the door of the lodge, and looked out.

"Everybody is running to the river bank," she called back in Shoshone. "Let us go and see."

Otterwoman said, "He might not let us. We might be beaten."

"If I am beaten," said Sacajawea, "I will know for once how I earned it." And she walked out of the lodge into cold open daylight, as bold as though she were not an alien, a slave, and of merely sixteen seasons.

She asked the others in Mandan what had happened, and they said it was an army of white men, maybe Spaniards from the country of the Osages. The wind was icy on the edge of the bluff; it blew the fringe of her dress back and cut her peering eyes. But her fierce curiosity surpassed even her other healthy appetites. All that had so far happened to her had merely beaten keener the edge of it. So, little and sturdy and proud with child as she was, she shoved her way to a place where she could see them—white men, coming!

Clark's red head topped the others; light caught the musket barrels and the bronze cheeks of the soldiers as they came off the boats. The other women and girls stared most at the godlike splendors of York; the huge negro looked to them like a great chief all painted black for the warpath; they hugged their terror of him and it passed down through them deliciously. But Sacajawea picked Redhead.

They came striding right past her, even he. Even Lewis, so careful to plan, so quick to see, so eager to find friends among these people. Even the men, who with sidewise glances appraised the squaws, passed over the little pregnant one. As they marched by her, the breath came whistling in between her teeth, so sharp was the pleasure of her wonder.

She was not present—who would have invited her?—at the ceremonial councils of the captains and the chiefs. But, womanlike, she caught at any glimpse of the adornment made for the occasion—the Mandans' rich embroidered shirts, their necklaces of elk teeth and of bear claws, the painted robes, the headdresses of hawk and eagle feathers, the quivers and pouches and pipes of ritual. She peeped after the white men, and saw how different they were from her own white man. How they were young, and straight, and how they laughed with no contempt in it. Then Charbonneau came, and kicked her into the corner.

Yet she stole off, at risk of more blows, to watch the white men dance, one night around their fire, to music sharp and jumping like grasshoppers. It was Cruzatte's fiddle playing a jig. The Indians laughed to see the white men jump and spin about, clap their heels and swing each other. Nobody could understand what they were dancing for. They were not dancing for buffalo or rain, nor to the Old Woman Who Never Dies, who is the Corn Mother. Truly, the medicine of white men was very funny, and there was no making it out.

"Sha-bo-no," said Sacajawea, sitting up when he wanted to go to sleep that night, "are the Yanqui people come here to live?"

"No, they are going away again," he answered her in

74

bad Minnetaree, the only Indian language he spoke. "Get down again; you let the cold in to me."

Sacajawea, always promptly obedient but always unquenched in spirit, slid under the buffalo robe and put her hands between her breasts thoughtfully; her tongue would not lie still.

"Then why are they building wooden lodges? They are cutting down the cottonwoods and elms and little ash trees with their iron hatchets. They make a great pounding." She was eager to tell what she had learned and seen. "They split the wood and sharpen it, and they make a wall like a fish weir, only closer."

"That's their fort," said Charbonneau drowsily.

"They take the big logs and they make notches in them, and lay the notches in each other, till the logs are like fingers set together." Under the buffalo robe she made a log house with her hands.

"Do you think that I don't know how a wooden lodge is made, that you should be telling me about it? Now be still. I have seen more than you have seen."

She was still while he breathed ten times, with a snore in the last breath.

"Sha-bo-no," she said very softly, at her politest and most cajoling.

He said, "Wnh?"

"Is the black one the chief? The women say so."

He chuckled sleepily. "No. A slave of the Redhead's."

"Is Redhead the chief of the Yanqui people?"

"He is one of the captains of this lot. The other captain is Monsieur Louis."

"They are not like the others who come to trade. They are more, and with big boats."

Charbonneau, as much a husband as any, was not unwilling to bestow information from his stock. "They are going on, when the river thaws. To the mountains."

Now indeed she lay very still. Her thoughts came out of Minnetaree into Shoshone like a spring growing clear, and looking in the crystal of it, she saw the far off, shining scene. She saw the snowline between green firs and blue sky, and the flowers of the bitterroot, pink and fragile, coming up through dark earth. Then she could remember the smell of cooking salmon, and the music of white water, living streams threading through clean boulders. And then the Shoshone language laughed and whispered in her ears, and she saw good faces around her again, and was once more a daughter and a sister and not a heavy slave.

"Sha-bo-no," she breathed, "will you go and trap and trade with them, to the mountains?"

"Will I go with them?" he said loudly, angry at being wakened. "Will I go with them, you say? I will go and sleep with a girl that will give me some sleep." And he got out of bed, and sought his Mandan woman.

But all the same, in a day or two he had thought over what Sacajawea had suggested to him. He did not think very fast, but he thought only of his advantage. He talked it over with Jessaume, the only man who spoke

76

his language and had a mind like his. Jessaume had been hired as interpreter by Lewis for the duration of their stay among the Mandans, but he was paid too by the Hudson's Bay Company man, to see that every possible obstacle was put in the way of the Americans. If he opposed Charbonneau openly, Jessaume reflected, he might drive the pig-headed fool into going with the Yankee expedition, and that Shoshone girl of his could perhaps help them to the Oregon country. So he merely agreed that Charbonneau might ingratiate himself with the Yankees and see what came of it. Jessaume was confident he could seduce the old fool from any engagement he might make.

Therefore Charbonneau came down from the village early in November, to the riverside where Fort Mandan was swiftly rising. It was a tingling winter day, with clean frost across the ground and a clean sky bent overhead. Charbonneau had piled four buffalo robes on Sacajawea and brought her with him. He carried his gun as a badge of standing and, as he came in to the officers, he began to adopt that manner, alternately obsequious and blustering, that he fell into whenever he came near English-speaking people. He bowed and shook hands with Clark and Lewis, and launched into a speech in praise of himself. Thereby it appeared that Charbonneau was a gifted linguist, a dead shot, expert waterman, wary trapper and had the heart of a lion. The silent mouth of Lewis suggested that that was as it might be, and the big Redhead laughed frankly. Waiting in the shadow, under

77

her burden, Sacajawea heard the laugh; she lifted her head, and they noticed her.

Quickly Charbonneau snapped his fingers for her; he then made a great business of presenting the buffalo robes to the gentlemen. Sacajawea, her back free, stood straight now and looked them in the face, her features still, her eyes bright with interest.

"This is my *femme*, here," Charbonneau explained her. "She is out of the Snake nation, a Shoshone. She is born where the Missouri rises in the mountains."

Lewis looked up from piling the buffalo robes. "So? Does she remember her language?"

"But perfectly." A gesture to the girl commanded her forward. She came up a step to be inspected, humble but to these white men dignified by her condition. The captains exchanged a glance, and understood each other.

"When will the child be born?" Clark gently inquired.

"Perhaps in Lent, gentlemen."

Lewis calculated, and nodded thoughtfully. He looked then into the young woman's black intent eyes; they were speaking to him, but he could not understand them. So he smiled, and Sacajawea felt a strange new thing she had not felt for any man. It was loyalty, conceived as suddenly as life is, and swiftly as vigorous in her.

The very next day the sergeant on guard called Lewis out to see a sudden splendor that was the Northern Lights. They rose, first pale and small, then widening and glittering halfway to the zenith, fading, then flung out again in shaken folds of radiance. Sometimes the streaks rose perpendicularly upon the horizon, and gradually expanding became legions luminous and advancing.

Sacajawea saw them too, and to her Indian mind no thing in Nature happened without meaning.

❧ VII

NO INDIANS CAME to the fort on Christmas, because it had been explained to them that this day was great medicine for the white man. The string of visits had been endless, prompted by curiosity, affairs of state, hopes of presents, and the desire to be hospitable. But for once the white men wanted to be free of the constant burden of ceremony, interpretation, diplomacy. None of them so tough that he had no tender place for Christmas in him, and none so free-living that he did not want to repeat old ritual.

The ritual of the southern frontiersman on Christmas, as of the southern mountaineer today, consisted in greeting the day with gunpowder, passing it with barleycorn, and stamping and dancing it to exhaustion before midnight. So the birthday in Bethlehem a thousand eight hundred and four years before was announced at Fort Mandan with two shots from the swivel gun and a round of small arms by the whole company, followed by a round of brandy served out by Captain Clark—here's to him! Then up with the Stars and Stripes, to astonish the lowering Dakota heavens.

Cruzatte tucked his violin under his chin, squinting his one good eye to it. Gibson tuned up his fiddle too; Ordway gave a polish to his horn with his sleeve and puffed out his cheeks to blow, and one of the boatmen showed how he could play the tambourine with knuckles, elbow, knee and toe faster than you could watch it. Rivet the Frenchman, like a boy about to turn a cartwheel, sprang on his hands and began to dance with his heels in the air.

The incongruous orchestra joined; its notes clashed, twined, and parted in an impromptu but courageous sort of counterpoint. There was but one real musician in the lot of them, and one truly sweet instrument; tapping his foot and nodding his head, Peter Cruzatte dragged players and dancers along with him into a tramping reel. The sound of the violin's bow and strings and belly, worked to mellowness with use and time, soared and sank and wound its way into the heart. The horn is the instrument for soldiers and huntsmen, the flute for the philosophic, the guitar for the lover. But it takes a violin to carry you back, and to say for men far away from home what they will not say to each other.

George Shannon stood looking on in the doorway of the big bare room where the men were thudding in their heavy shoes, unaware that he was not still smiling as he had been when the music started. His blue eyes were very dark. He was steadfastly pushing out of his mind the farm back in Belmont County, the fireside there and the laughter of Tom and John and James and Wilson and David, over the lighter gaiety of his three sisters. George was not a southerner and not a roisterer either. Jane Milligan Shannon's young began their Christmas day with family kisses and a grace. Then there would be carols, and they would be missing his voice. A strong young tenor, it had always led them. Always most himself when he was singing, George never loved his family more than when he felt the pillaring support rising from each young throat to hold the melody with him like a rooftree above them. Now he was glad that nobody proposed or seemed to know any carols; he couldn't have borne that. Then indeed he would have had to say to himself that he, an eldest son, was a runaway from the hearth of his widowed mother.

He was looking right now as young as he really was, and Billy Clark saw it. He slipped round the wall to come up beside him, and put his hand on the boy's shoulder.

"This'll be a day to talk about when you're a granddaddy, eh? The Christmas you ran up the flag to scare the wolves out of Louisiana Territory!"

George glanced round at him, swallowed and smiled; he couldn't speak yet.

"These are fine fellows we have," Clark remarked. "You get on with them well, I've seen. Take it at the flood, boy, as Shakespeare says. Life holds you up when you jump in and swim." He clapped him again lightly, as you might set a ball rolling, and Shannon, head up, stepped gracefully out on the floor.

At ten the brandy went round again; at one the gun was fired for dinner, and everything that could be called a dainty was brought forth. At two the gun went off once more, to call them all back to cavorting which went on, laced with doses of taffia or rum, till long after a sullen sun had vanished over the far away edge of things, till the cold set in and the wolves began to howl and the men to see giddy and a little red with their own blood's pulsing.

Charbonneau came in out of the night, his three squaws silent behind him. He went straight to the drink, and the women squatted in a row against the wall. The firelight and torch glow polished the copper of their flat cheeks and the inky blue of their hair. The Mandan had become gross; Otterwoman was sad and a little stupid; only Sacajawea sat straight and lively in her stillness, the obsidian almond eyes set shallow in her round young face, sparkling with reflected pleasure. Lewis noticed her, as he noticed everything, when he passed through the room—the little Shoshone, who might be useful.

When Charbonneau had warmed his vitals, he came and sat on a bench beside her. She turned her face up to him and asked, "Sha-bo-no, what medicine are the Yanqui dancing this time?"

"It is the Feast of the Nativity." He could say it only in French.

She looked puzzled. "What does that mean, in Minnetaree?"

83

"It means that everybody is happy because on this day a long time ago the good God gave us His little Son."

This was the first sense that Sacajawea had ever heard in white medicine.

"Who was his mother?" she asked interestedly.

"*La Sainte Vierge.*" Put into Minnetaree, it sounded like "the magic maiden."

"You are joking," she said.

He answered piously that this was not a matter to joke about.

"This maiden who could bear a child—what was her name?"

"Mary," he said. "She was promised to Joseph. Then the spirit of God entered into her, and she became with child."

"Was Joseph angry?"

"Yes, until she told him about the Spirit. Then he believed her, and when it was time for the baby to be born, a star appeared, very bright, and great chiefs came out of the East, with presents for the baby."

Warmth filled her at this, pleasure that the baby should have been honored and given presents. That was good; that was well done of the white men! She looked at them full of friendliness and new liking.

"Then it is this they dance?"

"It is this," he agreed.

The fiddle of Cruzatte jumped and sang; the notes of the horn stepped merrily about the room and the little drum flickered on the heels and elbows of the boatman.

84

The tired men still jigged and sashayed, reluctant to let go the hem of this day. Sacajawea stared at them, her racial immobility telling nothing. But within her, the little Indian drummed heels in a secret war dance.

Outside this tiny fortress of Christendom, all winter besieged the wooden walls with a vast paganism. From the arctic sea to Texas, from the Cascades to the heave and wallow of the Atlantic, there was only night and cold and wind, and the hungry running of the wolves and their howling. Each day thereafter took the Americans deeper into snow and frostbite; the boats were frozen in the ice, and even the stores of the rich Mandans were taxed when the buffalo moved south with a blizzard at their rumps.

In Washington, on New Year's Day, Mr. Jefferson, like most good presidents since his time, kept open house, poured a ready glass, and never started at the sound of vases and tables tipped over in the crush.

"Any news from that secretary of yours?" "And what word of the expedition?" "Have they sent you back scalplocks yet, Mr. President?" A woman's voice: "La, to think of that dear Mr. Lewis on such a cold day, by a campfire!"

"No, nothing yet." "A campfire keeps a man warm, madam." "I expect to get word in the spring, when the river opens. They will send a few soldiers back, I think, to St. Louis." "No, Senator, nothing as yet." "Thank you, your Excellency, I hope the Emperor's health is good?"

The Emperor felt indeed robust at this moment, having the most sanguine expectations. Napoleon had been Emperor of the French for a month, after a coronation unparalleled for magnificence and audacity. Pope Pius VII had been enticed and threatened to come to Paris to bless Bonaparte's impious pretensions; he had stepped onto the edge of the French crater with misgivings for the Church and for his person, having left instructions in Rome, in case he should never return from the atheistical land that had destroyed priests and sacred property in the madness of the Terror. But wherever he went through France, crowds pressed forward to kiss the red border of his white garments. Wax-pallid, ascetically chiseled, his shoulders bent with years of suffering for his children, the Vicar of Christ moved calmly, tenderly among the mobs, the new-made nobles, the soldiers with the blood of Europe just wiped from their bayonets, the squalor of the Paris streets, the Medician grandeurs of the old red pile at Fontainebleau, the bivouac splendors of the Tuileries.

It was here in the Paris palace that Josephine, under the seal of the confessional, babbled out to him all her smoldering shame. Though the world supposed her marriage to have received the Church's blessing, nothing but civil law, she told him, had ever been invoked. Napoleon had taken care not to undeceive the Pope about this. Now she, who had so cunningly left a loophole for exit from wedlock with a young adventurer, was

86

more than ever terrified, with the crown in sight, that it might be her husband who would slip free.

The sovereign pontiff, whom no common sin could astonish, turned to frost at the revelation. For this was no ordinary case of an unblessed couple; the honor of the papacy was at stake in a matter that history would write large.

Thus it came about that the conqueror was caught. Without a marriage ceremony, the Pope decreed discreetly, there could be no coronation. This was on the very eve of the event, when eight hundred empty carriages were deploying before the cathedral to practise their order of arrival and departure, when the carpenters were hammering last nails in the porches and pavilions and benches, the drapers were hanging the great nave with scarlet, the sempstresses were biting desperate last threads off velvet trimmed with pearls and ermine and lined with satin, the cooks concocting imperial pastries, the jewelers polishing the two crowns set with emeralds and rubies, and the master of ceremonies was parading dolls and marionettes, all he could buy up in Paris, upon miniature sets to explain to the courtiers their parts and movements in the morrow's spectacle. In the dead of night before the historic day itself, an altar was secretly raised in a chamber of the Tuileries and this man and woman whose embraces had so long ago staled were united in holy matrimony. Cardinal Fesch solemnized the rites, with the sardonic eyes of Monsieur de Talleyrand and Marshal Bethier for witness.

In the morning, salvo upon salvo of artillery announced the Emperor's departure from the Tuileries. Marshal Murat, at the head of twenty squadrons of cavalry, led the way for eighteen carriages, each drawn by six horses, filled with the kings, princes, prelates and ambassadors of earth. At the Archbishop's Palace, the Emperor and Empress changed their gorgeous attire for their dazzling coronation robes that dragged at their shoulders with a wealth of velvet and fur. The woman who had set the fashions of Paris now showed to the world the most splendid costume that cudgeled brains could devise. It was of silver brocade covered with golden bees; it swept into a train like a glittering river, leaving bare her shoulders. Her plump arms were tightly encased in sleeves embroidered with gold and adorned with diamonds, and a lace ruff worked with gold rose for a background to her curled and diademed head where pearls and diamonds vied with the jewels in her necklace, her earrings, her bracelets.

Borne by the measures of a triumphant processional, Josephine Tascher of Martinique, granddaughter of old Patrick Brown the Irishman, walked to the throne beside her husband, in the shadow of the altar before which Valois and Bourbons had been anointed as rulers. It is schoolbook history that at this coronation Napoleon seized his crown from the outraged pontiff and placed it on his own head. This looks like regal impulse, but it was craft, and stagecraft at that. And it was statecraft when he personally crowned Josephine, thus leaving her forever deprived of papal authority as empress. But all the bells of Notre Dame drowned out the truth of that.

So when the year 1805 was born, Josephine Tascher had become in seeming the most important woman in the world. A woman in her position might have shown mercy to millions, confounded knavish politics, fired the hearts of peoples, and as a consort held high a lamp before the world leader. In fact, however, chance had lit upon a poor shallow aging female, empty in head, heart and womb.

It is the curse and blessing of our human species that the fibre of a single one of us can alter the fate of all. No one can trace the lineage of Sacajawea, but she was nurtured by the force that makes the lodgepole pine so straight, the waters so white in the land she came from. She was born a piece of our aboriginal American Nature, which is our touchstone, and she was early mated with our race. But though it was Charbonneau who got her with child, it was not he who ever seized her soul. Lodged in the body of a New Stone Age woman that soul might be, but it was a great soul, and waited for great men to command it.

There on the wide plains knifed by Dakota winds they were, also waiting. They did not clearly see their way; they only dreamed it still, as Jefferson had dreamed it. But it lay mapped with the clarity of longing in her Indian mind, the river, the plains, the pass through the mountains. She could not tell the captains; she did not understand how they wished to be told. She was only a squaw, a girl of sixteen healthy years, getting up heavier each morning, falling each night to sleep with more eagerness to cradle her baby in her arms.

Like many a young mother's, her desire outran the unhurried workings of gestation. On February second she felt perfectly sure that today was going to be the day. It ought to be the day; she felt pains, and anyway she wished to see the child quickly now. The wise old squaws mocked at her and told her this was nothing.

Just when she really convinced them, the pains stopped. Every day after that she wished to be sure, and persuaded at least a few others besides herself, until everyone concerned was exhausted, when, on February eleventh, the baby really began to come.

This was not the easy birth we like to think is usual among primitive people. It was slow and hard, and even the Indians were worried. They told each other that it was no wonder, since a white man's baby must always be hard to have. They told the gasping girl to show now that she was a brave squaw, and her eyes and her teeth glittered.

But at last the old women were frightened by what they saw, and having powwowed together, some of them went to Jessaume, who could talk the white man's tongue to him. If the white chiefs had medicine great enough for this, let them bring it.

Yes, Captain Lewis, what have you got in your equipment so carefully planned, so minutely plotted? You who have been dreaming this expedition for ten years, did you dream of this? Do you understand that the whole success of your venture hangs on that girl's living through this hour?

And you, Mr. Jefferson, President of the United States, with all its ships and armies to command, inventor of gadgets useful and useless, you who dispute natural history with the Comte de Buffon and argue the rights of man with Tom Paine, you who penned the Declaration of Independence and planned the University of Virginia, down to a brick—what can you do about this? While you were writing out instructions, filling page after page with an easy flow of ink, telling your secretary to keep records on birchbark as well as on paper, to take observations of latitude and longitude, to note in detail rivers, climate, beasts, birds, plants, minerals, and all pertaining to the tribes encountered, whether of language, traditions, monuments, occupations, food, clothing, or prevalent diseases—why did it never occur to you to send with the expedition a doctor who could help this tortured girl?

For she was in extremity. Jessaume came in to Lewis, pity in his hard face.

"The little squaw, they say, will die if help is not found for her."

A look of pain narrowed the Virginian's lips. His active mind groped round amid his pharmacopoeia helplessly.

"Laudanum?" He thought it aloud. "But opiates, I believe, delay a birth."

"I don't know, sair, but I have heard the Indians say that snake rattle is very good for this. It might be; sometimes they know."

And I certainly don't, Lewis thought humbly. "Well, now!" he said, bracing his shoulders for encouragement. "That's a lucky thing. It happens that I have some rattles by me, cut for a trophy." He turned to rummage through the contents of a box, and thought prayerfully, as he hunted, give the little woman hope and faith, and God may help her do the rest.

He found the small, deadly singing rings, shook them once in his palm for luck, and set to powdering a couple.

They lifted her head to put upon her tongue the water that floated the powder. They said to her that the young white captain sent it, and she looked them in the eyes, her pupils widening till they engulfed the iris, and swallowed down the draught. Ten minutes later her fine big son was born.

ॐ VIII

HIS FATHER called him Baptiste, but his mother called him Pomp, which is Shoshone for "first-born son." When she was strong enough, she held him up and presented him to the East, where the sun rises. Then she turned and introduced him to the South, where the spring is born. Next she offered him to the West, where he was going, then to the North where the wild swans go.

Then she made a prayer to the sun and the moon and stars, and told them that there was a new life upon earth, and that they were to take care of it.

There is a new life, winds, clouds, rain and mist. Hills, valleys, rivers, lakes, trees and grass, I have brought you a new life. Take care of it. Then she prayed to the birds, great birds and small birds that fly in the air, and asked them to show the way to this new life. She summoned all heaven, all earth, all underground to take notice that she had made a new life—the word and the thought beat monotonous and strong as a drum, as she called upon the created universe to see what she had created.

The white men came of themselves to see it. The

rougher they were, the lighter they tiptoed on the puncheon floor of the interpreter's quarters. She lifted the blanket back from the child's head, to show everyone what a fine head it was, ruddy with a black down on it.

When Lewis saw Baptiste, the baby was as usual asleep. The woman, who could not speak to Lewis, and he, who could not speak to her, hid both their embarrassment. This young white chief, so stern and noble, so resolved and aloof, overawed Sacajawea, even while within her the strange new passion of loyalty secreted, day by day, drop by drop. In Meriwether Lewis she had at once perceived a chief to follow. But it was from her final hour of fire when she understood that it was his great medicine that brought her baby, that her woman's heart was pledged to him.

She could have made him a beautiful speech about this in Shoshone. She could have stumbled through something in Minnetaree, for the hateful Jessaume to say in Yanqui. But what she felt for the white chief was for no other tongue to profane.

So she was silent, with Indian dignity. Only her eyes spoke to him, dark, bright, watchful as a bird's when you look in its nest.

He straightened, smiling to the baby whose lids lay mysteriously closed in still nearly embryonic sleep. Every day of his training as a southern gentleman, from the time he was old enough to understand, told Lewis that this was the child of an inferior race. But every instinct as a man made him revere this rough bed. He, no less than Sacajawea, was overawed when he left her.

Clark tramped in heartily, beginning to talk halfway over the threshold. "So this is our youngest recruit! And going all the way to the Pacific, is he?" He bent down to peer, and as soon as he saw that all it amounted to was this tufted bit of tender red flesh squirming in its sleep like a naked new mouse, he burst into gentle laughter. The baby stopped squirming, opened its eyes, and gazed without focus serenely at distance. Clark slapped his leg in congratulation. "That's the finest boy in the United States," he assured the mother. He ventured a big cold finger into the baby's fist, and Pomp naturally clung to him. "Hey, there, let go!" Clark cried, pretending to shake him off. "Let me loose, I say! Wonderfully strong, isn't he?" he asked her, just as though she understood.

And she did. Every act and tone of big Redhead gladdened her. This civilized geniality was something she had never known either among her own people or those to whom she was an alien slave. But it came from Clark's heart, bright and warm and attractive as a camp-fire to a wild animal. She promised him in Shoshone that her son would give the white chiefs no trouble; he slept always and would be as light as a leaf in the boat.

Making a guess at her meaning, Clark said, "He's going to be a big chief, hm?" And he pantomimed puffing a pipe, strutting with importance and jabbing an identifying forefinger at the indifferent baby. The girl laughed outright, and he stopped, and came over and took her

95

brown right hand in both of his. He patted it, saying, "You had a hard time, didn't you, Sacajawea? Now it's over. You eat plenty—" he gave this order by signs. "You have to be strong for the baby, and strong for all of us. We may be needing you, when we get to the mountains."

Her hand fastened on his for an instant. In that passing grip he felt that she too had a need of him. Clark and Lewis had no particular love for her husband and, slave-owners though they were bred to be in Virginia, both felt disgust for the Frenchman's possessive brutality to the woman he had, by their order, legally made his wife during the winter. Now Clark shook her hand a little as in promise, and smiled into her eyes his championship.

A savage, to become a success in his calling, has to be trained from the day he is born. He has to start from the first taking all hazards and surviving everything that he is going to combat when he is older. The late Dakota winter of 1805 tried all its tricks on little Baptiste. Day after day the mercury in Captain Lewis's thermometer sulked below Fahrenheit's illogical zero, only changing when it would drop to minus twenty and minus thirty. The wind stormed and shrieked and gathered itself again to whistle in the chinks and up the chimneys. When snow flocked out of the sky, the wind caught it and sent it streaking without rest across the scoured plain, and when no snow fell and the day was so dazzling bright that even the Indians came in snow-blinded, the wind would pick the drifts from the prairie and carry them swirling away in the shape of shining devils. The boats were locked in the ice. The buffalo were scant. White hunters and red would come back from a ninety-mile chase with frozen faces and frostbitten feet. But the meat they brought was lean and tough in their cold bellies.

Baptiste slept with his mother's milk comforting within him. When she began to move about, he had the warmth of her back against his own. Swaddled stiff as a little image, he went everywhere with her between her shoulder blades. It was the lightest burden that had ever been carried there, so light with joy that her back felt the strength of wings.

The days lengthened grudgingly, but the grip of winter was still not relaxed. All the white men were impatient for the start. Whenever they had to wait like this, they found every discomfort harder to take than greater hardships on the move. Men had accidents then, but were seldom ailing; now there were pleurisies and coughs and rheumatic pains, and Lewis shook Dr. Rush's pills into his palm and tested hot foreheads. When the expedition was on the way, no one ever fell out with anyone else, and there were rarely breaches of discipline. At Fort Mandan there was constant trouble over women. Mandan women were part of the hospitality the tribe offered, but all hospitality has limits, and the squaws did not always go back to their husbands willingly. The two captains were realists, like any experienced officers; they permitted to the men what the Indians permitted to the women. They couldn't have felt responsible for the virtue of anyone unless it was the Shannon boy, who of himself showed a reserve like their own. So that these three, gentlemen born, having no traffic with her sisters, felt an affection the more loyal and intimate with the little young wife of their interpreter Charbonneau.

The geese began to go over. From higher in the sky than any other living thing will travel, fell their wild trumpet call to be off and away. Then the ice began to break. At night they could hear it grinding. Dark patches of clear water opened on the river, and the boats, long locked there, were now in danger. The men hacked them out and hauled them up, while the ice jammed and piled up on itself, and in the thin warm sunshine some of the men sat shelling corn, and others spread the trading goods to air them of winter's dank. The sky cleared off a pale, astonished blue. Rumor came from traders down the river that the Teton Sioux were gathering for rapine; they threatened, so it was said, to sweep on the Mandans and massacre the whites. The brant came down in slanting clouds to sail a little while upon the riffled inky pools between the ice floes, and be gone again north by the next day.

Time now for the teal to be coming, then the trumpeter swans, and after them long-billed curlew, black-bellied plover and great whooping cranes. Every day the ice was flowing faster southward, and more birds passed over it, going north.

It was at this time of break up, on the eve of departure, that Jessaume came scraping and bowing in to Lewis, with Charbonneau, nervously fingering his beard, behind him. Jessaume showed his palms and lifted his elbows helplessly.

"He say, *mon capitaine*, that he cannot go with you. He will not take orders, like the soldiers. He will go if he may leave the party when he pleases."

Lewis was icy. "I see through you both," he said. "You are an intriguer, Jessaume, but you cannot serve two masters. I am through with you now. Go back to the Hudson's Bay Company, and say so. I know they have never wanted us to reach the Oregon country, but the government of the United States is certainly not going to be stopped by you." He turned to Charbonneau. "Nor you," he told him.

Charbonneau began to wheedle. Lewis cut him short.

"You can either agree to accept the articles of this company like the other enlisted men, or get out of it."

The Frenchmen conferred, malice in Jessaume's face. Accordingly, Charbonneau lost his short temper. He made a vitriolic answer to Lewis's face, and walked out of the fort.

On his women he vented his anger. "We are moving," he said. "Pack up all my goods. We are quitting the roof of these bad whites. Get up. Get on with you!" And the toe of his boot went with it.

It took the women all day to move their master's trading store and household goods across the river to the

Minnetaree side. As she worked, Sacajawea's mind went thinking, thinking. So her husband now had made enemies of the white men. So he had taken her from them. So now, very soon, they would go up the river in their boats, without her. She would stand here on the bank, and see them go, and never again would she see the lofty snowline, the firs that pierced her homeland sky, the bitterroot that smiled to it. Implacably the opposition gathered in her. For the first time in her squaw's life, she began to think with her own will. Right here she parted herself in mind from Charbonneau. He has no honor, she said to herself in Shoshone. He is not of the tribe of the others. They are chiefs, and he is nothing.

Her eyes said all this to Charbonneau, and he heard it. Not for nothing are two people married. He could kick her, but he could wince at her too. And now those dark, true, piercing, inimical eyes made him see what a fool he was. A cat's paw for Jessaume—he perceived it. It was of good pickings that Jessaume meant to deprive him. Besides, it was cold out here, on the other side of the river. He missed the garrison fire; he missed the strength of authority bearing him toward success. Within a day he was back, whining before Lewis.

His first reception was so cold he backed away, really scared now. The next day he came in complete surrender, agreed to all orders, and made his women carry back to the fort all their many burdens. Lewis sighed in enormous relief.

On the first of April fell hail, the last pelting of winter. Rain came after, soft, pleading upon the rooftree, calling up out of the yielding earth the wet, dark odors of spring. Then a great night wind cleared the sky; the boats floated now on clear water. One of them was the big barge which was to go, as soon as the river was reliably ice-free, down to St. Louis with those of the men, under Corporal Warfington, who here left the party, and with reports and specimens for the President. Clark wrote out the invoice of these with his usual care-free spelling, while Lewis sorted and labeled and wrapped them, and Pat Gass hammered and whistled as he made boxes to contain them.

More than furs, bones, skins and Indian articles went into those boxes. Imponderable in transit, pride was consigned in them—pride of the beasts themselves, pride of the hunters who felled them, and the pride of lordly Mandans who sent their robes of state, their best corn and tobacco to the far away Great Father of the white chiefs. Along with all this went the chuckling boast that Americans feel in showing the world that ours are the biggest beasts and the tallest corn and the fiercest natives. The men of the expedition, westerners already at heart, thought, "That'll show 'em! What'll Long Tom say to those ram's horns? That grizzly skin? The tines of that elk I brought down myself for him!" And they spent some shots at nothing but empty sky, in homage to good game and a great President.

On the fourth day of April, the boxes were carried onto the barge and stowed there shipshape. On the fifth, the men loaded the westbound pirogues. On the sixth, the wind was gentle from the south, the skies were propitiously blue and mild, and Indians gathered, curious and full of good will, on the river bank. The seventh was the day of departure.

Corporal Warfington, with a handful of soldiers and a few French watermen, made ready to float the barge down the Missouri to the United States. These were good men and true and had done their duty, strengthening the garrison, and now, as agreed, they left this wilderness outpost to take last letters home and kiss their wives and girls there. Rivet was among them; he sprang on his hands and clapped his heels in happy farewell to the others.

Into the boats, two large pirogues and six little canoes, those others filed, thirty-one men, one woman and a baby. There go the Fields boys; they jump in ready as beavers for the stream, irrepressible McNeal, venturous Shannon close behind him. Now wiry Colter, and quick-moving Frazier; now the gunsmiths, Bratton and Shields, Gass the carpenter with the long Irish tongue to him, Drouillard the fleet halfbreed, and the three Massachusetts men, hard as granite. Now the French watermen settle to their places. Soldiers from the forts of Pittsburg, Vincennes and Kaskaskia shoulder their guns for the longest march they ever have faced. Now Clark hands Sacajawea, the baby in his papoose basket between her shoulders, into the rocking canoe, and Charbonneau gets himself gingerly in after. York follows his master, a black conqueror leaving behind his copper-skinned captives. Captain Lewis, on the *Experiment*, takes a last survey at the waters ahead, for vagrant ice. Then he snaps his telescope shut and calls the clear order.

Meriwether Lewis was by nature a melancholy man, tinged with foreboding. Some prescience made him always realize the quality of the moment. This moment, for once, pierced him with pleasure. What he recorded as his "darling project" now launched itself under an April sun that shone like his lucky star.

The keels went plowing their liquid furrows, breaking the river into light. Sacajawea, in the bow of the first canoe, felt under her breast the impulse in a homing swan's. The west wind greeted her face, and the sun falling westward was a beacon blinding in her eyes. Only the baby looked back, and did not understand what he saw—the straining men, the flashing paddles, the dimpling waves, the roof of the fort where he had been born, abandoned now and swiftly vanishing.

✿ IX

THE SPRING, so laggard on the plains of North Dakota, comes willingly to Washington; by April the front gardens are dressed in fresh green bordered with daffodils and squills and candy-colored hyacinths. Subsiding from the bustle of Mr. Jefferson's second inaugural, the capital looked about with seasonal restlessness for new topics. The newspapers remembered that they had been promised word, when spring came, of the expedition sent to explore Louisiana Territory. Congress, fanning away the southern warmth of May, requested to hear when Mr. Jefferson expected his secretary back? It wanted to know what was being done with all that money? It demanded to see some goods for payment received—two thousand five hundred of the taxpayers' dollars, remember!

But from the Great Bend to St. Louis, water has far to flow. No word came yet. There was nothing for the press to gabble over, except some fantasies let loose by inventive journalists, about a mountain of salt far up the Missouri, where mammoths wandered. These were ascribed, with ridicule, to Jefferson by a grumbling and defeated Federalist opposition. His interest in antediluvian bones, a subject on which he corresponded with the great Cuvier in Paris, was matter for scorn to minds that could not accept the evolutionary processes of both science and democratic progress.

But beyond our borders jealous eyes saw more importance in the expedition than did some of the gentlemen of Boston and Philadelphia. The Hudson's Bay Company and the Northwest Fur Company, claiming Oregon and what today is the state of Washington, were laying plans to swoop upon us if we reached the ocean. The Spanish, holding then all the lands between Texas and California, north indefinitely into the deserts and Rockies, feared—even more than Boone's advance into Missouri—the march of Lewis and Clark to the Northwest. So while they spun out negotiations over the boundaries of the Purchase, in a web of intrigue stretching from New Orleans to Madrid, they plotted to bribe the Indians against the Americans and secretly to send an expedition northward to intercept Lewis and Clark and turn them back.

Too late, you subtle Spanish governors, consuls, generals! Too late, ambassadors, court intriguers! The two pirogues, the six canoes with their flashing paddles have outrun the writ of any of you.

Where are they? Jefferson might wonder, longing to know. No human tongue could tell him, for not even the Indians, not the Assiniboins, nor the Knisteneaux or Sioux have seen them, neither their boats by day nor their campfires by night. But the snow geese have seen them, flying northward over the little west-bound fleet. The swans could trumpet to them, and the whooping cranes could cry it. The antelopes have fled them, and the beavers have slapped warning of their coming. The python river coils against them; the spring winds out of the West beat back their sails. Many a day it blew so hard they had to beach the boats and make a wind-bound encampment in the shelter of a bluff. When they were forced to use the towline, the tangle of bushes along the river trapped the men as they leaned against the rope, and fouled it; or the quicksands caught at their feet. When they used the paddles, they struck shallows or driftwood, and sometimes the blades became weighted as the water froze upon them. For spring was unwilling, uncertain; every night winter returned under the stars and stamped upon the earth and made of the wide air one vast dead blanket of cold.

The campfires, burning green or punky cottonwood, fought off this cold with dancing lances. A fire could scorch faces or warm up buttocks, but it could not cheer a chill like outer space. It could not keep the darkness at more than a few paces; within this shimmering circle that nightly made for them an insubstantial home, the men moved to and fro tiredly on rough domestic business, their shadows joining the wall of shadow that ringed them like an enemy. When they lay down at last and slept, the fire alone talked to the enormous silence.

The sentinels fed it, and it kept watch with them. As the hard heel of frost came down upon the deepening night, Scannon the dog shivered under even his heavy weight of hair, and rose from his place at the feet of Lewis, stiffly, and came with his ponderous soft footfall closer to the flames. There he lay down again, his muzzle on his forepaws, and stared at the fascination of the fire with eyes themselves glittering a mysterious red.

Then, every morning, again the river, the road that they cannot leave, for there is no other, the natural highway that runs forever against them. Other streams flow into it, streams so big they almost equal the Missouri in size, and must be measured in width and depth to make sure which of the two prongs is the master course. Smaller streams, rising one cannot think where, for it is a country of no springs, come crawling over the arid lands to lip against mother Missouri. Then at last come rivers of sand, great dry washes that have cut them a swath through the high prairie from unguessable distance. Yet there is no water in them now, or only stagnant rainpools. They spoke of a time when this land was better watered, but whether in a past geologic age or a past summer, it was hard to know. The thoughtful captains could not know that there was water moving in these dry rivers, for the water flowed at the bottom, the bed of sand was carried on the top. Sand was carried too in the air, in dancing devils and whistling clouds that gave the men sore eyes and drove inside their very watch cases. And there was smoke sometimes from smoldering fires in the earth, of natural coal, that Indians or perhaps lightning had set burning how long ago no man could know.

For time here was not yet man's time. It was seasonal, epochal, geologic. Yet, concentrated always on exactness, nightly the captains kept their records. Every night they wound their watches and the big chronometer. Every noon Lewis took a celestial observation to determine how far these mariners had come upon their arid seas. They measured out time as white men do, in minutes and seconds, and by breaking fast at seemly hours. But the Great Plains of America were as indifferent to their ticking measurement as Pomp, who got his dinner when he cried for it.

The party traveled with their guns always loaded, for not only had they to depend on them for daily food, but if this country belonged to anybody, it was to the Assiniboins, known to be the most inhospitable, treacherous and cruel of Plains Indians. All through the cottonwood groves, day after day, there was sign of them —ruinous fortifications, fallen lodges, and the bones of old feasts. But Sacajawea saw what the others missed. Here there had been so many men, she would say to Lewis through Charbonneau, so many women and so many walking children. They had had elk to eat, or dog, or here it was prairie chicken. They had been at this campsite seven days ago. At the next one seven

108

moons, at another seven winters past. The book of earth, across which men traveled like ants, had been her primer, and cleverly as an ant she could smell out the hostility of alien races.

Once they came to the burial of an Assiniboian squaw, if you could call it burial; wrapped in blankets, she had been raised upon a platform of sticks, out of the reach of snapping wolf jaws. Her combs, her mirror from the English traders northward, her jewels of glass, a handful of corn as provision for eternity, had been set carefully about her, close to her rigid hands. But the weight of snows and the winds of the past winter had pitched her headlong toward the earth; she hung half out of her bier, and the wind nosed at her wrappings. Her arms reached toward her dead dog, prostrate in sacrifice beneath the burial platform; the harness was still on him, by which he had dragged her here to lie alone with him in a spot that would be shunned by those who left her in it.

This was the way an Indian died and was forgotten; for time uncounted the wandering red race had individually gone back like this, with the slow rot and bleach of all natural things in this arid country, in anonymity to the dust of the West. Now, looking curiously as she passed at this desiccating sister, came an Indian woman who will be remembered as long as Americans love their country, for in its history no other woman ever served it better. So humble was her service she never tasted fame, and when Charbonneau called to her to come away there from the dead Assiniboin, she came as quickly as an obedient animal.

Everywhere this land, at once so fertile and so barren, at once so soft with winnowing grass and rotting poplar, so fierce with wind and fang and arrow, lay wide and yet incredibly deserted. Only once an Indian dog came to them across the prairie and cried for human companionship. And once Sacajawea said she could discern three fingers of camp smoke wavering into naked blue. But when the white men looked, they could find only horizon.

Every evening while camp was getting settled, Sacajawea would take a sharp stick and walk out on the prairie, little Pomp snuggled upon her back. There she would dig for wild onions or, better still, hunt for sign of the prairie gopher, and when she found it she would rip open the roofs of the little burrows to thrust in a quick brown hand. Out she would bring a store of sunflower roots, that are succulent as potatoes. But best of all she liked to find the five silvery leaves held up like fingers to show her here was the *pomme blanche*, the Indian breadroot. It wasn't so good now in spring as later when the flowers begin to fade, she told Lewis. He wrote down in his record for the President all that she told him of its uses, and he put some leaves of it in his press, that a Latin name might be added to its names in Crow and Sioux and Mandan and Shoshone. The men had come to eat with satisfaction these foods Sacajawea got them out of a land that looked to their eyes sterile; they liked the taste, too, of having with them a woman who concerned herself thus earnestly over their comfort.

Now the country grew ever rougher and more desertic. Yet the game was plentiful as though this were the day before the Fall of Man. The buffalo were so ignorantly unfearing that the men could walk within easy range before the herd stampeded. The antelope, out of curiosity, would come to a man as soon as he lay down in the short grass and waved a white rag on a stick. The beaver were taken in hand by the French trappers. Nightly a good smell of roasting singed the milder air.

Shannon brought down a wading bird, and carried it by the legs to Captain Lewis, who guessed it was some plover. He ruffled with interested hand the black and white plumage softening to pink over the head, and fingered the odd new uptilt of the bill. This dead avocet's strangeness spoke of the unknown ahead, and so did the gathering driftwood and the great gummy cones floated from forested heights that were not yet so much as cloud banks in the west.

Sacajawea began to scan the muddy banks with thoughtfulness; she found tracks and brought Redhead to see them.

"So they walk in my country—big, like that. The bears in the Mandan country are cowards. In the mountains it is they who take the warpath against the Indians. One of your bullets will not be enough. They live and fight with many arrows in them." She said it proudly. "You have to kill them right through the skull before they will die for you. And that is hard, because there is thick muscle where the head sets on the neck."

Bratton, one day gone out hunting, came back at a winded run and tumbled into the canoe so breathless that for some minutes he could not tell them of the mile and a half that a wounded grizzly had chased him; they found it later in the bed it dug itself to die in, and it was as big as Bratton had described it. The men felt pleasure more than fear at the grand audacity that this new country now began to show them. It had climbed up out of plains into wide plateaux; the rocks that basked in Maytime sunshine had been slung here out of unseen mighty ranges, and the river scouring the rocks was colder now, clearer, richer in volume. Now grass-root no longer touched grassroot.

The first sagebrush putting forth new leaves began to silver the land. Sacajawea smelled it before it could be seen; when, after so long, she reached it once more where it spread out westward like a tranquil ocean, she broke its leaves with inner devotion, crumbled them between her fingers, and breathed the scent up hungrily into her nostrils. What this brought back to her, and what it promised, filled her breast that swelled with her greedy inhalation. But among the thirty-one men there was not one to whom she could have talked of this; either they lacked the tongue or the heart to understand her. So instead she sang it to the baby, very softly, a

Shoshone song about his ancestors, the Lemhi men who spear the salmon and own many horses, the proud tribe of her father and her brother, who keep the pass that is hidden in the Rockies.

X

"LAWD JESUS!" groaned York, sinking to rest on his back and elbows, his soles to the campfire. "Mah bones is jelly! How fah we come, do anybody reckon?"

John Colter drawled, "It comes nigh being dead reckoning as ever I want to see."

"Doan' talk lak that, Mastuh Colter. Doan' talk 'bout dead. Hit's a good thing we ain't dead this night, after all them ruckuses. I never figgahed on gettin' et up or drownded."

"Would you rather lose your scalp, when we meet up with the Indians?" This from Shannon, as he walked into the circle of firelight and leaned there on his gun; for all his smile, his fresh young face was looking drawn tonight.

"Liker to lose his head entire, over the squaws," grunted Gibson from the other side of the fire.

"It's a powerful long time between Indians," ruminated McNeal. "A queer thing—when you don't want 'em they're thick as fleas, and when you're huntin' for 'em and need 'em, there ain't one in a thousand miles. And game's plenty, too. Where they hide out?"

"The woman say," reported Drouillard, "we shall not see them till we come to her country."

"They skeered plum out o' heah by the b'ars, like me," said York.

The tired men relaxed in laughter over the black man's fear; it made a useful butt for them, keeping their own down as they jeered him for it.

"I noticed," George Shannon teased again, "that as the spirits went down, the spirits went up." And the boy moved off laughing toward the officers' fire, where he wanted to listen as Sacajawea, through Charbonneau, was teaching Shoshone words to Lewis.

"Faith!" said Pat Gass, gazing after Shannon. "That taffia rum Captain Clark served out never warmed a colder belly than I had." And he shivered in retrospect at the day behind them.

They had all been tired out when even the first of the two accidents hit them, and dusk was then already coming near. Cruzatte, who had been a hero in the second, now turned to John Shields. "If it take six men to one bear, it ver' good thing the bears do not all attack at once, like Indians."

"This fellow was sleeping when we seen him first," Shields put in. "The Fields boys and me and Bratton here, and Colter and Potts seen him lying on a bank, sunning hisself like a baby."

"Baby!" snorted York. "Whuffo' go pokin' up black Satan?"

The bear, four bullets in him, had charged the six men, roaring as if the bullets had been bee stings; they shot again, and broke its shoulder, but it came on all the angrier before they could reload. Two jumped in the canoes, two fled and hid in the willows, shooting, but every shot seemed only to direct the raging grizzly to its hunters, so that a couple of them, cornered, dropped guns and pouches and leaped to save themselves down a twenty-foot steep bank to the river. After them plunged the bear, and it nearly had John Potts, when Colter from the willow fired and got it in a vital spot.

"I took it mighty kindly of you, Colter," Potts murmured sleepily from close to the good fire. "Time we two git in any kind of fix again together, I hope I shoot as smart."

John Colter turned to Cruzatte, "Peter near did better'n me with my b'ar today. 'Most shot a man who needed it, didn't you, Peter?"

"That *imbécile* of a Charbonneau—he cannot swim, he cannot steer, he cannot keep his head. When the squall hit the canoe and turn her, he luff her up into the wind, the fool! So she fill with the river like your hat, and three men nearly drown. And all that Charbonneau can do is cry to the good God and all the saints to save him. God does not think it worth His while, so I, Cruzatte, must do it."

"Your threat to shoot him if he didn't take the helm

116

was the one thing brought him to his senses," Bratton said. "We near lost most the gear that Captain Lewis sets such store by."

"I was standin' by the cap'n when he seen it, on the bank," York said. "I had to hold him back from jumpin' in the river. Drownded suah, he would 'a' been, in those rapids. Lawdy, my Saviuh! What a day! Sweet Jesus, watch an' bless us!" He got up then and devoutly kicked a log that sprawled out from the fire, till the sparks like golden bees went swarming upward toward the chilly stars.

York's master, Captain Clark, was in a mood as thankful. He was a man to whom one adventure was as good as another; the important thing was that you should not go through life beggared of them. That is, you should always drive toward a goal beset by difficulties worth the fighting. In Billy Clark initiative was effervescent. So that army service had come in time to pall on him, and so had the affairs of family property with which he had perforce been occupied, when the letter came from Meriwether Lewis that asked him to share command of this expedition. Clark seized the chance with instant certainty that it would ask of him all the best he had to give his country. His broad shoulders gloried in the charge laid on them.

His friend, he knew, who took responsibility as confidently, felt the weight of it to be a greater strain. Tonight the flickering light dug shadows deeply in the lines from nostrils to the corners of Lewis's mouth. Clark, seated in the shadow, watched him lovingly, as the younger man listened intently to the impetuous Shoshone on the squaw's quick lips. Now it seemed to gabble, now to whisper, like the talk of grackles gathering in spring to go far places and to brag of doing great things.

"*Tabba bone,*" repeated Lewis gravely, "*tabba bone.*"

"What is that?" Clark called, hitching a little forward to the fire.

" 'White man,' " said Lewis. "Those are words we all should know, I think. The lot of us are so tanned now by the weather we might well look like a redskin war party to the Shoshones, if ever we come up with them."

Clark pushed shirt from belt to show a break of milk-white middle. "*Tabba bone,*" he owlishly intoned.

Sacajawea's eyes were merry. She was happy. She loved to hear her language on the lips of the white captains. Every day now, she knew—by the old sore memory of her captive drive into exile—that she was coming nearer to the place where the wind also talked it, among the spruce boughs and running through the grasses where the lilies blew along the mountain ridges.

"*Sa'i,*" she said now, which is "good" in Lemhi Shoshone, "*Sa'i,* my captains."

A slender shadow moved out of the night and came into the firelight—a tall boy and a long gun.

"*Tabba bone!*" Clark greeted Shannon. "Come to the powwow, lad! You're not too old a dog to catch the trick of this lingo."

George Shannon laughed, and came forward to sit where Lewis welcomed him to share a log.

Not one of them knew just how well George caught all the lingoes of this expedition, even the *patois* of the boatmen. He had a musical ear and a talent for tongues, and nothing had so delighted him secretly as to hear Captain Clark holding forth heartily in his Virginian English to some leather-faced Arikara. "Ah am dee-lighted, suh, to accept this token heah of yoah friend-ship foah the gove'nment of the United States, and Ah take now the pleasuah of presentin' you with a jah foah Madam yoah squaw." Young Shannon could have par-roted the softly curled diphthongs as exactly as the Ver-mont accent of Frazier, who rolled his R's before him like apple barrels and twanged his N's like the strings of a banjo.

George leaned forward now to listen for the Indian woman's words, to catch the whispered final vowels like grace-notes, and the clicking consonants. The Lemhi speak Shoshone more rapidly than any others of that nation, with the accent falling on the first syllable of the words, so that to the white men it sounded faintly ur-gent, like a wind hurrying through brush or seeds shaken in a pod. George memorized the words Sacajawea now was repeating, but his thoughts, like his eyes, were on the girl herself. This very day he had asked her how old she was, and with her fingers she had shown him the num-ber of her years. Seventeen, like his. He showed her that by friendly signs, but hid his astonished feelings.

119

At the beginning of the journey, when he was first flushed with the pride of being a man among men such as these, she had been to him inconsiderable and alien. Today, when she had been quicker than any of the lot of them to save the precious instruments and medicines out of the river as the canoe tipped, he had felt for her a sudden ardor of admiration, like any boy's at a heroic action. What astonished him was the reflection, strong in him now as the firelight burnished her copper cheeks and black braids, that she was, after all, a girl of his own age.

The girls of his age back home might be plain or pretty, common clay or porcelain, but they were banded all together in a secret sisterhood, a web they spun of charms, privileges, pretenses, behind which they hid and peeped at him. He had tangled with that web as often as any likely lad of good looks and good blood. He had ever a ready answer to the invitation of lowered lids, of parted lips, of a tress twined round a finger. But being Jane Milligan's son he showed respect to those who deserved it, and good sense with the others who needed that.

They were an absorbing thought, the lot of them, when there was time to think of them, and somewhere, he hoped, a particular white sweetness waited in bud till he should blow upon it. But not one of them could have lived through the trip from St. Louis to the Mandan villages, or through the winter at the fort. You wouldn't have thought of taking along a white girl; she wouldn't have left her feather-bed and her father's roof, to burn in the sun and wind by day and sleep with the cold at night, to the song of the prairie wolves.

Sacajawea, Canoe Launcher, in her fringed deerskin dress belted with blue beads, her hard thick braids falling with pride over the swell of her breasts, was woman, essential, natural woman. She was innocent, ignorant, of conscious charm. Glad of food as Scannon, she tore it with her white teeth greedily; when her baby was hungry, she fed him as gladly and frankly, the round bronze apple of her breast bared even to the north wind. Had you had her in a heated, scented room, she would have smelled Indian, but here in the clean coldness of the Montana night, she was no dirtier than he, George Shannon. Her dark eyes glittered like the night sky behind them. She had no need to hide and peep and play at mystery. She was mysterious as woman is to any lad who has never had a woman.

This girl George had seen by day and night, bearing all the fatigues and accidents, the small human humiliations of travel and the sudden calls upon resourceful courage and quick-witted initiative. Among all the men she had complained the least—which was never once. She considered herself exempt from nothing, privileged in nothing. Whatever she did, helping to beach a heavy pirogue, drag firewood, skin bear, she did with a more thoughtless skill than any of them, and always with the burden of the child in his papoose cradle on her back.

The farther they came into wilderness, the more she

showed herself to be the guiding feather upon this arrow into the unknown, which was the expedition of Lewis and Clark. Here, returned from exile, she was in her element. She was part of the fauna, the free and fearless populace of beasts and Indians to whom this land still belonged, whatever the treaties dripping red seals might have to say about it. A mother animal with her cub, she sensed, still far off but always coming slowly nearer, an old trail, a known scent, that would take her back to the lair she came from. And this uncommunicated knowledge gave her a new eagerness, a new pride, a new bright beauty.

The lesson in Shoshone having been concluded, Captain Lewis arose and thanked Sacajawea formally, through Charbonneau, for what she had done this day.

"If you had not saved the instruments," he said, "I do not see how we could have continued this journey. I want to give you something to show you that we thank you," he concluded, in the style that he knew was pleasing to Indians. From the pocket of his coat he took a string of beads, of different colors of glass, and presented them to her.

Sacajawea jumped to her feet and took them in her hand with childlike pleasure. She held them up to see the firelight polish them; she displayed them to Charbonneau proudly, and it seemed to her that fire and the sun and the light of the stars all flashed from the depths of these mysterious and priceless jewels. She put them on her neck, immediately took them off to examine them incredulously in her fingers, slipped them again over her head and caressed them as they lay upon the deerskin.

Charbonneau arose stiffly; he was not glad when his wife received a present and he did not. But tonight he had nothing to say for himself. He knew that Sacajawea had made herself a heroine in the eyes of the captains, and that he was today sunk low in their estimation. In spite of all Sacajawea had been able to save, quantities of medicine, flour, and other irreplaceables had been lost to the river through him. And tomorrow there would have to be a long delay while the Indian trading goods were dried out in the sun. All his fault! He said to his woman curtly, "Come to bed. Everyone is tired. You have talked too much."

George watched them go, the girl obedient after her master, the little papoose blinking sleepily at the departing fire, and a nameless heat rose up in his throat and flushed his cheeks with darkness. He told his officers a respectful good night in a strained voice, and left them.

"You made the little woman mighty proud, Meriwether," said Clark, warmly approving. "She's a woman like the rest of them—takes to gewgaws like any queen." He chuckled and poked the fire.

Lewis bent down and found his little writing desk; seating himself on the log, he opened it in soldierly routine. No matter how many miles they had slogged, no matter how the body begged and demanded the quick surcease of sleep, that journal nightly was brought up to the hour. He scrutinized the quill's point, dipped it in the tiny inkwell, and paused to answer.

"I ascribe to the squaw equal courage and ready good sense with the best of the men in the party. Yet she is content with a handful of glass beads. She seems to want no more than that and food when she is hungry." He began to write swiftly.

Clark had his own journal to keep up, but he dwelt a thoughtful moment with smiling eyes on Meriwether's bent head. Will that lad, he thought, ever really know the heart of a woman, red or white?

He regarded his friend as a brother younger yet far more gifted than himself. The learning and polish of Lewis, the way he guided his course hotly by a cold star, filled Clark with mingled admiration and amusement. And he loved Lewis the more tenderly because Lewis would not show a need of it.

Now, as he settled to write himself, Clark remarked, "Two new rivers discovered this day. What have you chosen to call them?"

For they named every creek as they came to it, descriptively or perhaps for one of the party.

"Why not call one," suggested Lewis, "Brown-Bear-Defeated Creek, as the Indians would have it, in honor of our victory over the grizzly? I have not thought what we shall call the other; it seemed to have no traits to mark it."

"Name it to please the little squaw. 'Sacajawea

Creek,'" Clark offered, smiling. "This was a day to remember her for."

Lewis paused in his writing, and looked up, away, into the dark of the cottonwood grove. "Well, now," he agreed, as though it surprised him a little, "I think that is just. That is just indeed." He nodded, consideringly, "You'll mark it then upon the map, Billy?"

For it was Clark who drew the maps and made most of the sketches.

Charbonneau was in vile temper, all the worse because he had no one to blame but himself. He did not speak as Sacajawea arranged her bed; he waited until she settled herself there to suckle the child for the night. He chose this time, malignantly, to quarrel with her because he knew it was a moment dear to her, which left her particularly vulnerable. So now he said, in Minnetaree, "You are getting too proud and too bold. You think the white captains have some regard for you. Let me tell you they have slaves in their own country, and they buy them and sell them like blankets, just the way I bought you, and can sell you again."

Sacajawea did not answer; her lids fell heavy and Indian over her glittering eyes. The baby made greedy sucking sounds for a minute, and then Charbonneau attacked again.

"You are so fond of Redhead and Monsieur Louis. Very well, then, I will take you to them, and you can sleep on their blankets!"

A quiver went through the woman's shoulders as

though Charbonneau had used his rawhide on them, and her answer was stung out of her. "They would not touch me," she said proudly. "The Arikara chief brought them his wife to show them hospitality, and they sent her away with him. They were disgusted. It is not thus that white chiefs conduct themselves."

Charbonneau had never meant what he threatened; he meant worse, and had been leading her into a trap. "If they will not have you, there are others. You saw how some of them behaved among the Mandans. They are men like other men, and here there are no other women than you. They will pay me as they paid the Mandan fathers and husbands."

She plucked the child, wailing, from her breast and got up. "You I despise," she said in swift Shoshone. "You are the droppings of a coyote. You have not the courage of a rabbit. You are as stupid as a toad, as feeble as a maggot. I spit you out of my mouth. If you ever touch me again"—and this she said in Minnetaree—"I shall kill you with a knife between the shoulders."

Then she took up her blanket, put the baby to her other breast, and walked through the circle of the firelight and beyond it, till she came to the tent of the captains. There she found Scannon, sleeping outside it, and she spread her blanket beside the great Newfoundland, and lay down close to him, her arm around her baby.

❦ XI

SLOWLY, each day by a little, by degrees of changing Nature perceptible to the watchful eyes of the captains, the expedition toiled into new high country. They saw that even the sagebrush was giving way to greasewood, that shrub with an inflamed fleshy tissue like a salt-marsh plant but growing on lands that Lewis called the thirstiest he had ever seen. Every few days they struggled through a cloudburst, but the soil was never slaked; it glistened white with deposits of alkali sometimes as far as eye could see. Now even the cotton-woods were scarce, and often fires must be made of buf-falo chips. Now the cactus waylaid them and stabbed through shoes and moccasins; at night the men had thorns to pick out from their bleeding feet. In all the world there is no vegetable so surly and inhospitable as the prickly-pear, leafless and sprawling and ready to sting as a coiled rattler; it cursed the land where it grew, and was cursed by the men who suffered through it. Yet because even here May was yielding to June, and that is the time of flowering, this demon plant flowered too, with great pink cups like water-lilies afloat upon waterless space.

Every day the river was becoming harder to navigate. Almost never now the sail, and the paddles only for crossing the stream. Almost always the towline, and the toil on foot along banks now flinty, then plucking at the heels with mud, or bushy with red osier to the water's edge. Time and again, sometimes half a day together, there was no footing on the bank at all, and the men must labor through the shallows to draw the canoes after them. The water was icy, colder than it had been in April, for it came chattering from distant snows. So they would be up to their armpits in a roiling, treacherous flood that chilled them to the bone; yet on their heads the sun of these great waste places beat with an endless blow.

With constant towing, the elkskin ropes were fraying thin and slack. Clark and Lewis spoke of it only together, but they feared hourly that one of the sharper boulders would gnaw through when the strain was crucial. Then the hapless boat would shoot backward down the rapids, to be inevitably smashed and all within it lost. Clark had twitted Lewis with the *Experiment* from the day that it arrived in Louisville; its ribs of iron were stout enough, but the whole cumbersome contraption, when you had to tow it, was like a burden of sin. Now Clark ceased to chaff his friend about it; instead he consoled him.

The two captains watched the men with grave eyes,

unless a man looked their way. Then either was ready with a confident smile and a terse word of praise. They saw the recruits grow thinner these days; they saw, as the days lengthened with the lingering of the sun, as the heat increased and the tortures of cactus, mosquitoes and blow-flies intensified, that exhaustion came very close to the stoutest, long before nightfall. When there was a halt and an order to fall out for rest, men dropped asleep on the rocks in the broiling sun, within thirty seconds. The captains felt as though they were measuring out their chief resource, beside which neither powder nor flour weighed so precious. It was more than the sheer physical stamina of the men. It was more than their obedient courage. You can form collective courage as you can mass lead soldiers; when Marshal Ney flourished a commanding saber and shouted, *"En avant!"* he set the brave ranks of Napoleon's armies marching against the Spanish people, or the Russian people. He didn't have to explain to them why this was a good thing to do, or whether it was good at all. Courage had been conscripted, and drilled to die unquestioning.

But it's our way to ask, if we have to be brave, "What for?" And when we know why, nobody has to wave cutlery at us. We'll keep it in mind; we'll be there when they get there.

So that each man under Lewis and Clark was in himself a captain, of his will and body, calling like a leader on his every last resource. For the whole party was inspired by a comprehension of the greatness of their purpose. They were conscious that they were attempting, by their combined will and skill, to prove the advance of their nation by thousands of miles. In our system any rivulet can contribute as much as any other.

The two captains toiled as hard as the privates; they would hunt afoot twenty extra miles in a day to provide game for all. They would clamber up every cliff and butte to survey the land for mapping. And they saw farther than their eyes could, farther than their men were able to see. Already both leaders realized that there was no faintest hope of reaching the Pacific and returning to the Mandan forts by winter. A year at least of wilderness lay ahead, with every likelihood that from here on all would grow harder.

So, just as they wondered how long the elk rope would hold, Lewis and Clark scanned anxiously the line of their twenty-nine men. They watched the swelling of shoulder muscles where the naked backs bent all along the towline, and the look in the eyes under fallen lock and dripping forehead, and how the lips drew thinly back in effort from the teeth, into the Yankee grin we give our enemies as we fight them. No, the rope was not breaking; nor did it ever slacken.

Ten years ago Thomas Jefferson had told the boy Meriwether that he proposed to send a lone man to the Pacific, and Lewis had accepted the dare in a flash. It was ignorant of them both; it was quixotic; lucky it never came off. And yet Meriwether Lewis, with thirty men around him, still traveled solitary. That was his nature. Clark knew it; no one was ever nearer to him, but even Billy Clark accepted the fact that Lewis must often be left alone. He must be permitted to scout ahead, all by himself, without Clark's showing solicitude or eagerness to go. Time and again Clark stayed with the boats, directing and urging, taking responsibility for those nutshells laden to the rims with all the gear of existence, while Lewis with his telescope under his arm went prospecting up the buttes. Now as the river grew more rapid, now as the air was suddenly sharp and clearer than any American had ever seen before, Lewis seemed to his friend possessed of a fever. For years Lewis had longed to hear the heart of the continent pulsing, vein and aorta, eastward Missouri, westward Columbia, where these life-waters separately burst forth from a summit hidden beneath the Great Divide. To reach the source of greatness a man must climb. And they had been climbing many months now, up the vast slow tilt of the country, three thousand feet up, across the Great Plains.

One more butte Lewis went to clamber; a flock of bighorns nimbly leaped away before him, dislodging never a stone. His own rougher footfall was solitary in the enormous sunny silence; his eyes were on the trail he picked out through the rock. He reached the summit; the west wind came blowing and lifted up his face, and far to the southwest he saw his heart's desire—the Rocky Mountains, a long blue line shining, beyond the shimmering waste of space yet to be traversed, like a farther shore. He whipped his telescope up to his eye. They marched to meet him in a stride. One hundred and twenty miles away as the eagle would fly it, the wild tossing of the Little Belts flung skyward. Their bases swathed in heat waves, they rose to a dark band that Lewis guessed to be needle forests, and higher, into crests of snow valleyed with pale green patches that would be meadow. He wheeled slowly, shoulder and arm and head moving with the spyglass like part of it, to follow the sweep of the waiting Rockies across the horizon, incising on his mind every serration, every peak and slope of their outline. And suddenly he discerned beyond, behind that first bold range, another, a farther, fainter but unguessably higher range of mountains, touched with a glint like another planet's. He lowered the glass, snapped it shut, nipped it beneath his arm again, and stood, his hands clenched tight behind his back. The wind out of those mountains crossed that arid void that he must cross, reached the butte, ran through its grasses laying them about, and with a flick in his face and a whistle in his ear went past him lightly.

Meriwether Lewis took in the deepest breath that ever filled his lungs. Blown from the snow fields, it came into him like ice and was turned to fire in his blood. He let it out slowly, like a prayer. Then he could swallow the great lump of the years of waiting. So they were there, the Rockies. They were not a legend, not a hope that you must die to realize. They were a fact as clear as this morning. They were seen of his living eyes, here and now, on this young summer day in his thirty-second year, where he stood, feet planted apart on solid earth, braced to a wind that cut him with reality.

Just twice before had the Rockies been seen by white men, by Coronado to his despair, and by the Verendryes whom they defeated. Others pretended to have reached them, drew up fantastic maps with ranges and rivers born in imagination. Lewis had by him such maps on the journey. But a month and more ago he had perceived by his noon observations, taking latitude and longitude on the trackless plain, that these maps lied to him.

So he saw again, looking the Rockies now in the face, that he must find his own way through them. He perceived the hardships as certainly as he saw the high dim outline of the ranges, but he would get through, he knew quietly, if the luck was with him.

Better than luck was with him, in a sturdy Indian body, in a heart that longed for the Rockies with a passion more informed than his. But Lewis could come back to camp that night and watch her oil her hair with bear's grease, amusedly, and never think to tell her he had seen the shining mountains that, but for her, might have proved too high even for him.

He regarded her as she took the baby out of the papoose basket and unswathed its squab-like body. Pomp drew his knees up luxuriously and kicked with pleasure. First she washed him in water with her hand, close to the fire; then, once he was dry, she oiled him with the bear grease, and when her fingers got in his fat creases and tickled, he crowed with mirth. Captain Lewis, young Mr. Lewis, sometime secretary to the President of the United States, Meriwether Lewis, heir to Locust Hill, stood on a tussock of sand-rushes in the wildest wastes of Louisiana Territory, and looked down on this primitive Madonna, unaware that he was smiling, or how far he had changed. Woman to him had meant dashing and witty ladies like Theodosia Burr and Dolly Madison; he had bent with a courteous appearance of interest over more than one infant lying on a satin cushion. But the pain of this halfbreed child's birth had not been hidden from him, and daily, hourly, beneath his eyes there had gone on for months the rituals of natural mothering. The more he saw of this she-animal and her cub, the more human he became.

Next day, in a place where the river came shooting down between bluffs, boiling with whirlpools and tossing up over boulders big as houses, in a fine high anger, he had the luck to sight from shore a noble prize. If there was anything needed now, it was elk, more for its hide than its meat. This was a magnificent doe, accompanied by her fawn, that leaped into the flood at sight of Lewis on the riverside. The proud creature swam powerfully through the torrent, keeping the fawn upstream of her, her flank a bulwark to its lighter weight. Lewis drew a bead squarely on her, and then for the life of him he could not pull the trigger. He lowered his rifle; the doe heaved dripping out of the flood, the fawn stiff-legged and nimble after her, and both bucked lightly up over a log and away into the bushes.

But it was Billy Clark who had a way with the baby. By this time he considered himself part of Sacajawea's family, and told her so in English. This was the only language he ever used to her, and she understood it as well as Scannon did. He had come to call her "Janey," and she answered to this readily. So that when he held out his burly arms at a noon rest by the mouth of a river that Lewis called the Bighorn, and said, "Janey, let's feel how fat young Pomp has got since last I dandled him," she promptly put the baby in his embrace.

He weighed it judiciously up and down till it crowed and grabbed at his nose and lips, then tossed it back to her, and taking her by the shoulder, said, "Come along here, Janey, we want you to look at some moccasins and Indian truck."

They went together along the bank to a point where Charbonneau and Lewis were examining several pairs of worn moccasins found in a ruinous stick-lodge. Sacajawea picked them up with eager interest. She examined their cut and beadwork closely, and then dropped them on the ground.

"Those were never on Shoshone feet," she told her husband. "Atsinas, I think."

"And this?" asked Clark. He held up a crude football made of buffalo hide, which he had fished out of the stream as it came eddying eastward.

"No," she said. "That is a Pah-ke thing." She looked at it with dark scorn. "They must have been up the river, stealing again."

Charbonneau relayed her answers to the captains in the miscegenation of French and English on which they got along together. He stood there, in his rotting leather dress, a little stooped and very hairy, like a beast that could walk on its hind legs—less of a white man than many an Indian. Yet at this job of interpreter he was at the best he could reach; as waterman, scout, or hunter he fell far short of all the rest of the party. But when he was translating he was in a sense trading, which was the one calling for which he had a gift, and he took a squeeze both ways, trying to make Sacajawea think that the captains spoke to her in contemptuous words, and the captains that she answered stupidly.

Lewis was not deceived. He said, looking at her kindly, though he must speak through Charbonneau, "It is a long way to the country of the Shoshone people, very much farther than the Mandans described it. Are they to be found in those mountains we are beginning to see ahead?"

"In the mountains beyond those mountains," was Sacajawea's answer.

So they toiled on again.

It rained; the men plowed on through icy water to their chests; a hemp towrope broke; the mud sucked so they could not wear their moccasins. The wind was contrary, and the current high between the enclosing rocky bluffs. And they apologize once, if you please, in their journals because they dragged their laden boats that day only twenty-three miles!

Soon the land began to show what it could do to over-awe men so bold. The river came curving and bridling down through badlands. They were of ancient sandstone, drifted here by desert winds, compressed in colored strata, carved by pitting sands and by the cloudbursts that are this country's manner of rainfall. So all this land was sculptured into columns, into nameless idols set in alcoves hollowed out in the lonely buttes, where violet shadows overlay Indian red. There were swollen domes, their pedestals half eaten by the ages, and minarets awry. Surely gods, thought the exultant Lewis, have lived here and departed! And he raised a rapt face, where he sat in his pirogue, to watch the crying swallows lift from the nests that honeycombed the walls of these ruins, and at the white men's coming also depart from here.

Through this country of stony, desertic grandeur, repeated like hallucination variously at every bend, tore the river, more ominously silent than when it gabbled over rapids. Here it was deep, and had become so clear that the black rocks in its bed lay like sharks down below the keels.

Once out from this fever-dream of the badlands, the expedition burst forth upon uplands refreshed with springs, where summer had just come. The low grounds along the river were abloom with wild roses, and at the limit of the plain the snowy mountains rose visibly nearer, range above range, for all the men to see. Around them spiraled the songs of birds, of western meadow-larks that juggle ten shining notes up into the sunshine and down.

Then the captains, who had spent long winter days with the Mandan chiefs learning what rivers would come in, from right and from left as you went up the Missouri, looked ahead and gasped. For here, rolling south across the highlands, came a smooth confident stream that no one had told them about. Perhaps no one knew of it. Yet this was a notable river, as broad as the Missouri that bore them. Equally, to the north and to the south, the shining water forked. Which fork was the one to take?

For they must make one right, immediate judgment. There was no time to waste, since already two months of the short northern summer season were behind them, nor was there flour or powder enough to provision a mistake.

Clark and Lewis descended from the bluff where they had been surveying the ambiguous streams.

"It's win or lose right here," said Billy Clark bluffly, "as much as ever on the spin of a coin."

"The south fork," Lewis ruminated, "seems to head from too far to the south. The north bears more directly toward the mountains, yet it is muddy-looking, as if it came from country with deep soil. The south is clearer. I confess I'm at a loss."

So they spent five precious days sounding both rivers, to determine which had the greater volume, the broader spread, the slower current. Puzzling over the maps again one night, Lewis exclaimed.

"Here, what's this?" he inquired. "Here's the river that I named the Big Horn. You have changed it. 'Judith's River,'" he read, and suddenly laughed. "Come, who is she, Billy?"

"You can name any stream the Big Horn," Clark evaded genially. "This one is Judy's."

"Do I know the lady?"

"Such a little lady!" Clark's lips were tender. "She will take it to be a mighty honor to have a stream marked with her name on government maps. A child of the Hancocks, Meriwether, of Fincastle in Virginia. *Aetat* thirteen."

Lewis, as he smilingly agreed to forego his Big Horn, thought how his friend loved women and children with an equal purity. Then he frowned, and drummed restless fingers on the map.

"Billy, we can't prolong delay. We must take our decision—make a choice between the forks."

"The men, after their prospecting, are unanimous. They vow the north fork is the true Missouri."

"I know," said Lewis, and he shook his head. "But I stand out against the lot of them, for the south fork."

"And I am with you. The little squaw cannot be shaken, either. She must have been a child when she was

139

driven into exile, but she insists the north fork will take us into Blackfoot country."

"Then the three of us must be right for the men. This is one more confidence we must ask of them. May it prove justified by the event! I'll go ahead up the south fork, to scout it out, if you think well of such a plan."

"Excellent," Clark agreed. He reached over for the map. "So the north fork is declared to be the tributary. By what name, then, shall I mark it?"

"You took the Big Horn from me, for your little Miss Judy," his friend replied, with a twinkle. "So I shall claim this river for another lady. Mark it 'Maria's River,' Billy," he directed, and his voice went light and quiet.

Clark's eyebrows rose, quizzing. "A rather muddy stream, I'll venture, to celebrate a lovely fair one—if such she be?"

"On the other hand, a noble river," countered Lewis, not rising to the bait. "It has been vying with Missouri itself in our consideration, for many days. Mark it down, Billy, mark it down!"

Clark, as he sketched the letters, cocked a narrowing eye at Meriwether who sat writing; rapidly he ran through his acquaintance with the Lewis kith and kin. In far away drawing rooms and ballrooms he sought for this Maria, among half-forgotten faces, and names that whispered to detain him. Then all at once he thought that he had found her. Maria Wood, was not that the name? A cousin, he believed. But he could not persuade to return out of limbo more than the shadow of a slender

The first is whether he can come across on television. "I'm not good on TV," Mondale admits. "It's just not a natural medium for me." Part of the reason is pure cosmetics. A reasonably trim man, Mondale's face invariably looks heavier than the rest of him and television cameras seem to heighten that jowliness. His eyes are dark blue and set in deep, permanently smudged sockets. In the esthetics of television, the lack of contrast translates into two distant dead spots in the middle of his face. The way his voice rises and goes nasal when making a point is a drawback as well. More central to his video difficulties, however, is Walter Mondale's own uneasiness with the medium. He s uncomfortable assuming the star

Forward the
Nation

F592
L7P3

figure, a lovely face half averted. She would not turn her head for him, but he remembered long white fingers moving over ivory keys. Maria. There was some melody flowing from those fingers to entwine itself with the name. Half recollecting it, Clark began softly to hum.

Abruptly, with a nervous reserve like any wilderness creature's, Lewis flung down his pen, got up and strode away.

XII

HUGH McNEAL was limber steel for the work of the expedition, for beaching a boat, setting a doughty pole in the river bed, or bending his back at the towline. He was a lively wit around the fire at night, a man who not only did his full share of work by day but gave more than his share of cheer when the day's work was done. He comes we don't know whence, and in the end he would go no one has discovered where. He was just one of the twenty-nine on whom Clark and Lewis could count every day. With some little humor they note scrapes he got into and scrambled out of, when off duty, and there is always the shadow of a squaw in it somewhere.

Nor was he the only one with a taste for the Indian women. Ordway and Gibson and Goodrich, to name some names, took what was offered, without blame from their captains. This was a man's world, from the Wood River all the way to the Pacific, and back— nearly three years of it. Save the boy Shannon and the older Gass, the men of the party were all in their young twenties, all unmarried but Charbonneau, and they were under terrific strain for months at a time. They were so deep in wilderness now there was no turning back, not even in thought. Drenched to the neck in river water, you could not dream of a clean shirt, not while you had the evil tricks of the current to keep under your eye. You could not think of white new bread while you gnawed at tough buffalo or old bear, or it would stick in your craw. Even at night you dared not remember home and its sweet decencies, for there was sentry go to do, and the grizzlies were so thick in the brush that every night the men had to beat them out of it before they settled down, and even then they kept big Scannon padding all night long about the encampment, on a sharp-nosed watch of his own.

There were no women for them then, and no thoughts of them but fleeting remembrance. But whenever there was a halt long enough for the men to rest and think, women were there, in the men's heads if not in person. The twenty-nine would dance and stamp away their desires, at times like these five days spent where Maria's River joins the Missouri, with Cruzatte's fiddle making a song for them of arms about their shoulders and soft cheeks against their own.

So these stops were always a time of possible danger to the high-strung morale of the expedition, and the captains knew it. But they didn't know what Charbonneau, sensing his moment, was suggesting, to the ones whom he knew susceptible.

He began with Hugh McNeal. That lively lad opened

his eyes, swallowed hard, and was angry with himself to feel the tomtom of his heart against his breastbone.

"I don't understand you!" he shouted in English. "I can't understand your lingo." And with a hand against the trader's chest he thrust him away as if he were too busy to be bothered with him.

So Charbonneau went among the others. They were taking thorns out of their feet, or stretching weary shoulder muscles; Goodrich was pottering over his ever-lasting fish lines down by the river, and young George Shannon writing in his diary, that has been lost to the world. To Alexander Willard, Charbonneau spoke apart, and he intimated that the object of his bargain was willing and personally attached to the prospective purchaser.

Willard, when he grasped a little of all this, lifted a big New England fist. "You old polecat! Get out of here or I'll break your numskull." And as Charbonneau turned away, he gave him a kick that the trader bore in silence, storing it up among the odds and ends he was keeping to swap.

When he came to Ordway with his proposition, he got a still harder jolt. Charbonneau knew from observation how far was this New Hampshire man from a saint, but Holy Virgin! he had never guessed how close he was to a devil. The powerful sergeant grasped him by the hair and beard and forced him onto his knees. "By God!" he said. "You Judas! Do you think one of us in this camp would do the thing you ask? Somebody should strike you down dead." Knee to belly, he knocked the shaking Frenchman to the ground.

Charbonneau's bleat of terror brought Goodrich from the river bank, in his hand a line with three fish on it, and from farther off came George Shannon running.

"Here, what's this about?" cried Goodrich, staring at Ordway kneeling on the prostrate Charbonneau's chest, menacing his shrinking face with a ready fist.

Ordway explained, in frank language. Goodrich's slabsided face broke up into furrows that worked with anger. "Why, for two cents," he said, "I'd wring his neck, the old crow!" And he swung his line and slapped the cold fish across Charbonneau's mouth.

Ordway looked up and saw the boy standing there, his face white and his eyes blazing darkly; he looked lost to reason and really dangerous. The sergeant warned him, "Stay out of this, youngster! You go tend to something you've got to do."

"It's plain what ought to be done." George bit off speech, and strode away to do it.

"Captain Clark," he began, as he came up to the officer who was sketching a dead adder for the records, "I beg leave to report that the fellow Charbonneau is going through the camp offering his wife to the men. And from what I have seen"— his voice rose with a lilt of rejoicing anger—"they will soon kill him for it unless you intervene."

Clark threw down his crayon and got up at once.

"Thank you, Shannon." He strode past, without his usual smile.

"You may get up, Sergeant Ordway," he called as soon as he saw the sergeant in action, in the midst of a ring of watchers. "Peter Cruzatte, step up! I shall need you to tell this man something plainly in his own language."

Charbonneau, with a bleeding nose, puffed eyes and unsteady knees, crawled up onto his feet before his commanding officer.

"The captain says," Cruzatte translated to him, "that if Monsieur Louis were here, you know very well you would get a hundred lashes, the way the deserter did. He tells you now, and he says you had better listen to it, that if this ever happens again, or you strike your wife or you show her any least unkindness, he will treat you as a traitor in the army, and shoot you dead."

The men dispersed, not talking to each other about what had happened, wanting to forget it. But long minutes afterward their anger still burned along their veins, and hottest in the men who most promptly frequented the Indian villages when they reached them. For them the casual squaws were not too good, not too poor, to satisfy necessity, since nothing better offered, two thousand miles out from any white settlement. But man loves woman, too, wherever he finds himself. And it was their love that had been outraged, their respect for a comrade who daily proved herself as good as the best man among them.

Shannon went apart, among the cottonwoods along the river, to discover what this was that had come boiling up in him. For a space he couldn't see what he looked at. The sunset light was black for him, and there was a rushing in his ears that was more than the water's. With his knife he fiercely attacked the bark of an old cottonwood; first he cut the rough outer cork down to a smooth surface, then he began to whittle this patch of naked trunk to a perfect plane and, as he did so, his mind cleared and quieted.

He couldn't, he saw, have got much angrier if it had been one of his sisters who was insulted. And yet the Indian girl was less sister to him, less of his own kind, than any other woman he knew well. As to romantic sentiments, he had none for her, of the kind a boy has for a girl. But he had left all the girls in Belmont County to follow a higher romance than any in petticoats. And it was of this that Sacajawea was a part.

From the captains to the privates, all the men of the expedition spoke of a boat as "she," a gun, too, as "she"; even a watch or a compass is always of that gender. For such things are of woman's kind; they are sensitive and require deft handling, and they complement a man and make him whole. Sacajawea, Canoe Launcher, was like the captains' precious circumferentor, like its living needle, dark and true, that quivers and yet is steadfast.

She was not only their guide forward, but by her womanhood she brought them nightly home. They would come frankly crowding, laughing, to watch little

Pomp when he was let to kick a while upon the firelit blanket. The resolve that this baby should get through to the Pacific and back, safe in their charge, had become one of their acknowledged objectives. Some of them carried about in their breasts a belief in their need for this little life, like a lucky piece. Pomp, then, belonged to thirty-one men and one woman, and so his mother belonged to all of the men too, to care for and be proud of.

But Shannon the boy saw her better than any of them, as her separate self. Since the day when he had found her age to be his own, he had gone wondering if that could mean to her the bond that it meant to him. Sometimes when her dark eyes flashed excitement to him, over a rapid well run or a bear killed in the nick of time, he was sure of it. They two were companions in youth, among a more hardened lot. Had he looked back, had he had a girl at home to dream of, he might have wondered at how beautiful he found Sacajawea.

Her coppery skin was beautiful as the wet rocks gleaming in the sunshine, her breasts had a brave young lift to them like the rise of the land. Her braids he loved, for the way they fell straight down from her head, sloped in pride over her bosom, and swung free with every stroke of her paddle. He took a secret pleasure in her sturdy figure going ahead of him, with a step so much lighter and surer than his or any other American's, and in the way she carried herself, true as a solitary pine. George Shannon, when he ran away from book lessons, had lost his ardent Irish heart to the unknown this expedition went to find out intimately. Out of that unknown came Sacajawea. So George loved her, and it was not so different from the passion with which Meriwether Lewis looked toward the Rockies.

On this day Lewis was vouchsafed certainty that he was driving straight toward that backbone of the continent. He was scouting ahead, alone, up the south fork. Back in his mind lay the warning of the Mandans, the promise of Sacajawea, that the true Missouri was marked out from all rival rivers by its falls, three broad cascades, one above the other, with swirling rapids between. The Great Falls of the Missouri would be proof of the right road, as they would be a bar across his passage. Every pound of goods, every canoe and instrument and gun would have to be portaged circuitously, painfully, past them.

As he strode over the crowding hills and rolling prairies, there came to his ears a distant threat that shook the summer air, a throbbing hope that made his heart beat faster. The endless talk of the waters he followed rose far away into a song. Suddenly a gust of wind swept past him and out of a blue sky drenched him with a cloud of spray.

So mighty are the Great Falls of the Missouri that, from the moment their distant reverberation caught his ear until they broke upon his sight, lay seven long miles which he covered with a quickening stride. Now, tired and triumphant, he sat beside the cataract that was so

149

notable a milestone, nursing his knees and his lonely satisfaction.

This, this, his flying thoughts exulted, he alone of all his kind had ever seen before. This salvo of cannonading, this calamitous splendor, had been no white man's through eternity, and now was solely his. By crashing step and step the river, like a wild stampede of horses, stumbled and reared, tossed head and mane in the descent. The spray of it forever leaped in air, was caught in a wind of its own making, twirled in wraiths that gestured, joined, melted away, and were formed over again. Through the spray played a rainbow, not that tranquil arc that bridges stormy sky, but dancing flames of color flickering like lightning through the water's thunder.

Alone, remote, unwatched, Lewis surrendered to this pure and savage spell. The shouting waters drowned out reason, freed him from the discipline he kept upon imagination. His thoughts went with the torrent, reckless, dissolving, the exultation of his immediate achievement working like alcohol in his blood. So he dreamed, too soon, of his rewards. He dared, rashly, to taste all that success would earn him—the fame, the honor, the riches, and that ultimate reward, the woman to whom he meant to offer all the rest.

Leave him there, prematurely living what he would never live out. Leave the girl alone too, playing Purcell to herself for comfort, in some far drawing room. The sorrows and the secrets left behind by Meriwether

Lewis are not ours; only the grandeur of his accomplishment is public property.

Jefferson was the first to get a tangible proof of its progress. On this day there had arrived, to his delight, those boxes that Pat Gass had nailed up at Fort Mandan in the first days of April. The President opened them himself; he was the kind of man who likes to pull a nail out without bending it, and not even a servant must see what was here before he did. Even before he saw it, he smelled it. The rankness of hides, the pungence of stuffed specimens, the stink still lingering in the Indian clothing had come along in the boxes too, all the way down the long Missouri. Jefferson sniffed it with interest. No label, no accompanying invoice could have proclaimed so clearly that these spoils came out of new lands harboring undescribed possessions.

He took from their wrappings with eagerness the skeletons of badger, squirrel, prairie wolf, weasel and the first antelope ever collected in America. Then he lifted out a variety of peltries, the frosted wealth of the grizzly's skin unrolling to incredible dimensions over the library floor; he stepped ardently around the prostrate monster, to admire the enormous claws, the yellowish fangs.

Next it he spread the buffalo robe painted with scenes of battle between Sioux and Mandans. He knelt enjoying this, hungry to be told the whole of its meaning. The rude artist had depicted chiefs with headdress feathers of the hawk and eagle, stolen horses, squaws with arms spread out to show amaze and admiration, strutting braves who pointed with their lances at a direction where they had bested enemies too numerous to draw.

There were other boxes, from which the President lifted a Mandan bow and quiver of arrows, an ear of their spotted corn, various seeds that his gardener's hand weighed appreciatively, and some pressed specimens for Dr. Benjamin Barton of Philadelphia to analyze with his Linnaeus. The appetite of this naturalist-President was merely whetted by the litter around him. "These," he thought, "come only from the threshold. Now they are over that, and far beyond it."

They were well away now into country where no tiresome concerns could ever overtake them. All that they would be seeing was pre-Adamite in its namelessness. Whatever they put out a hand to gather would be treasure to natural science, for every step now was the white man's first.

Thomas Jefferson pondered this almost devoutly. His mind was, in part at least, a scientist's. This part dwelt harmoniously within his cranium beside that part of his brain which was a statesman's. The expedition to the Pacific, conceived in the mind of this statesman-scientist, was the first of its kind in the history of land exploration. There had been other scientific outfits to gather curiosities for study; there had been voyages of conquest innumerable. This journey was new because it was a journey into the future.

Thomas Jefferson, better than anyone alive, foresaw

more than the fur trade for which John Jacob Astor was looking, more than the thwarting of the claims of Spain and Britain, more than a window to the western sea. He knew that this nation was planted to grow. He himself had penned some of the words that give it growing room. Some countries may grow by rapine; some may not grow at all and be proud of it; and some there are so old they have fallen, decayed, sprung up again from ancient rootstock. But this one was planted, deliberately, in sod deep enough for a mighty root system. There may be dry rot in some of our branches, but the trunk is sound, and still growing skyward.

When we Americans cease to live for the future, then will the heartwood be dead. Jefferson's America had the widest frontier in written history to open; we have got through now, all of us, to the Pacific. If we stop there, if we rest satisfied that the fat lands and the fine cities we have planted are purpose enough for a nation so conceived, so dedicated, then we are done, and we deserve to be.

If you think we have reached our last frontier, then the course of this nation is run. Then we have shown, in growing populous and rich, all that there was to us. We can begin then to enjoy old age, count our securities, and in time fearfully watch them diminish. If all that we have got is for ourselves alone, then we are just what angry men at home and elsewhere call us. If we are afraid to set forth where there is no precedent to smooth the way for us, then we are not worthy of the men and women who went where there was no path.

But there still rise up, among the many rest of us, a few who can perceive shining mountains yet unexplored. They dare even to propose to go there. And you who admire the twenty-nine men who went with Clark and Lewis, you who are tough and lithe in mind as they were in body, you will not hold back, when such captains call us into an unknown future.

✑ XIII

HOWEVER BAD this pain gets, Sacajawea thought, I must not give any trouble. She felt she had given enough, at the time of Pomp's birth; and now, recently, when the white men had been so angry at Sha-bo-no, the whole camp had been in a turmoil. She had been ashamed to be the cause of fighting; she should, she told herself, have managed Sha-bo-no more quietly. He was afraid of her now and would make no more mischief. But something good had come out of all that trouble, just the same; it was a new feeling in her heart. She had never imagined before that she mattered to these men, except as the wife of Sha-bo-no, who might be useful—and, she proudly hoped, as the mother of Pomp.

But what she was enjoying was simply that position among men to which every white girl feels herself born. She had started out with the party from the Mandan villages as a slave, of an inferior race, little more than a beast of burden. Surprised, the captains admit in their reports, and the men in their diaries, that the squaw bore up under every hardship with a cheerfulness and courage the equal of the best. They show how they came to depend upon her, to read for them sign of game and possible enemies, to find them edible plants, and forever to point them true. So she became a comrade. And then, as night after night she with her baby made a niche of domesticity for them all, she had become family.

She herself barely guessed this; she might not have understood it wholly, since the pattern of the white family was unknown to her. What she did recognize, by the instinct of her own good blood, was the aristocracy of the captains. Their qualities as highborn Virginian gentlemen were not wasted upon this wilderness Shoshone girl. Race in them as well as rank called up her devotion. Next to Pomp, whom she served with a natural passion, her foremost thought was always of her duty to the two chiefs.

She was not going to give them trouble now, she repeated stubbornly. But devils were biting her belly, and her head had bees in it. To an Indian, one is never sick from what we call a natural cause, but always through the ill will of the supernatural. So Sacajawea had to suffer without help, as she lay in the bottom of the canoe, or on the ground at the halts, with her baby in her arms. She told the men to pay no attention; she would feel better in an hour. But the hours lengthened out, and day by day she grew worse. Captain Clark gave her that specific on which the expedition trusted in any indisposition—Dr. Rush's pills; he told her they were compounded by a great medicine man in the East, to banish all kinds of devils out of you.

But these were very bad devils. The white medicine man could not have known about them, for his medicine did not drive them out. They writhed like snakes inside her, and the bees in her head stung. Little Pomp wailed all the time beside her; her sickness must be spoiling the milk, and it was this made her afraid.

She saw the sky above her, but there was no longer any color in it, to her eyes. It seemed to her that the boat spun round and round in a whirlpool. The rush of the waters and the shouts of the men, sounding too loudly in her fevered head, made her believe that they were plunging forever into rapids. She was terrified that, should the canoe upset, she would not have the strength to swim to shore with her child.

If only Captain Lewis would come back from the Great Falls he had gone to find! He alone had medicine great enough for these devils. This was a time as bad as the time when Pomp was getting born, and he had saved her then.

At the noon camp, when they had carried her into the shade of a tall rock, Clark came to tell her that they could hear the Great Falls now. She answered him, but she could only think of Shoshone and no one knew what she was saying. Charbonneau, looking grave, spread his palms apart and shook his head. They sent for Shannon, who had picked up from her more Shoshone than anyone. The boy knelt down beside her, and was suddenly chilled to see her white moving lips and the rapidity with which the braids on her breast rose and fell.

"Sacajawea!" he called to her softly. "Speak to me. Tell us how it hurts you."

She made an answer, but he could not hear it; he slipped an arm under her, lifting her up, and her head fell on his shoulder. He put his ear near her lips. The Shoshone words went whispering like night wind through the brush; they clicked like seeds falling from a broken pod.

The boy raised darkened blue eyes to Clark. "I don't hear it well, or I don't understand it," he said, "but she says, 'food' and 'child' and 'water.'"

"Delirious, perhaps," Clark said, "since she speaks no Minnetaree." He gently lifted one of her lids with his thumb, and searched for her pulse.

Shannon watched him frown, watched the thumb and fingers move up and down the slim brown wrist, groping for the faint life-beat. "Is she dying?" he asked hoarsely, and without knowing it folded her close in both arms.

William Clark shot a thoughtful look at the Shoshone girl and the white boy. "She's an Indian, remember. They can last out a lot. Put her down, lad, and come with me. We've passed a number of mineral springs here about. You and I will just go look for some. The waters might help her." Shannon laid her gently back upon her buffalo robe,

"Watch out for the baby," Clark told Charbonneau. "We're going to find some medicine for your *femme* Janey."

Charbonneau called upon the saints to bless them. He spoke with a fervor they hadn't heard before.

Now she could not remember even the baby. Now the tomtoms of a spectrally painted medicine man were beating. He was trying to slow down her pulses by beating just a little slower than her heart. But the throb of her blood was winning. Now he was blowing tobacco smoke into her nostrils—a waft of the camp smoke had crossed her face—to give her back life. And now the medicine man and Captain Lewis must be holding her over a fire, she thought, to draw the fire out of her flesh. They swung her slowly above it, pulling her legs and arms while she shut her lips upon moaning.

Lewis, wiping the sweat off his forehead, looked down at her and said to Clark, "Good God, Billy, this is bad!"

He had walked in on them, on this seventh day after his departure, jubilant with news of the falls and sure of the portage. But the faces he met had no smiles to greet him. It was Jo Fields, the gayest daredevil of them all, who miserably blurted, "The squaw's sick, Captain, and like to die."

So Lewis saw for himself, as he stood looking at her. Over the rolling plain the wind of midday came blowing, with nothing in it but desolation. The sun glared down unhelpfully around this little puddle of shade where the girl lay panting.

"We've given her sulphurous waters from the springs," Clark was saying. "Nothing among our stores did any good. If the Almighty put them here for any purpose, those springs were meant to save this poor young creature."

Young, thought Lewis, yes, the poor thing is very young to die. He had a fatalist's mind, and could face and believe in such a dread possibility. The rest went around swearing defiantly that, by God, she mustn't! Clark made within himself an honest prayer to the humane and warm-hearted Divinity that was his. But Lewis thought, and if she doesn't live? What becomes of the poor infant? We cannot feed it. We cannot leave it to die. So we would take it with us and watch it die.

And suddenly he had the disastrous feeling a man has when his most essential instrument is broken.

Yesterday, near the top of the falls, he had been at- tacked by a grizzly. He had flung his rifle up to his shoulder and pulled the trigger, only to find that he had forgotten to reload. In that instant all that stood between him and bloody destruction had been a weapon as good as a dead stick. He had fled eighty yards, the monster gaining upon him, before he thought of the river and remembered that a bear cannot attack while it is swimming. He plunged into the icy rush and turned to face the bear; for some reason he could not fathom, the grizzly stopped a moment, measuring the man's defiance, and then broke into a lumbering retreat, never stopping till it was out of sight.

So Lewis stood his ground now, and faced the calamity of this girl's possible death. He perceived more clearly than ever, in this moment of danger, how much he counted on her. He was so near now to the mountain Indians, wherever they would be hiding, that Sacajawea's worth lay suddenly as plain before him as her condition. Was the key to the door to be dashed from his hand?

Melancholic and fatalist Meriwether Lewis might be at heart; outwardly he was always the commanding officer, undeterred by setbacks, responsible for the morale and confidence of all. So that night he pretended to a jaunty frame of mind. "I'm cook tonight," he told the men. "Get out the flour, York, and you, Drouillard and Labiche, get to work with your knives on the buffalo carcasses and cut us out the choicest steaks and the tongues."

And thus did Mr. Lewis of Locust Hill, secretary to Thomas Jefferson, at the foot of the Great Falls of the Missouri, mid-June of 1805, make thirty-one dumplings and serve them out with a flourish, one to each grinning man.

"And when we have finished," he promised them, "all such as can still shake a leg after a march like to-day's, if Peter will strike up his fiddle, shall trip the light fantastic, as the poet says." Laughing, he left them for the shadows where he need not laugh.

Whether due to prayers, oaths, fatalist's courage, or the sulphurous waters, by morning Sacajawea was better and clear in her head. Then Charbonneau, to hasten back her strength, acceded to her demands for food and plenty of it, and stuffed her—contrary to the captains' orders—with dried fish and a quantity of *pommes blanches*. And so in no time she was worse again.

Now Redhead's temper got away from him. "You blundering fool!" he cried. "If your *femme* dies, now it will be your fault. And as there would then be no further use for you on this expedition, you could expect to be left here to the wolves and grizzlies, for all it would matter to us."

He went off stamping, and Charbonneau, nervously fumbling in his beard for some excuse, believed his threat.

But Sacajawea, still intent on doing her duty, did not die. Hers was a vitality uncorrupted through timeless generations. Her ancestors were a people who could fight with the shaft of an arrow still in the neck, who could run twenty miles on feet that had been blistered over torture fires. They lived on muscle when there was nothing to eat, and survived month-long orgies of overeating when there was game. The winter snows of the Rockies were mere dew to them, and it never occurred to them to consider heat in the blazing Montana midsummer. As for sickness, they didn't even believe in it; they called it devils. Health was their daily right.

Sacajawea's whipcord body cast those devils out. In

another day she was up with a laugh. Pomp was peaceful again, chewing his fist to finish off the dinner in his little belly, and his mother, to show the men that she was useful as any of them, promptly went off to catch fish for everybody and eat her own share of it afterward.

The portage around the falls, only a few miles long, took two weeks to complete. Every ounce of all their goods, every boat, including the iron pirogue, had to be dragged or carried around the three great cascades. They built a skid-road, up over the hills and down, and with logs and poles they made rude *travois* and carriages.

But even so it was grueling toil. The sun beat on their heads and the backs of their necks with hammer blows; their feet were pierced with cactus spines, and all the while they could see the snowy mountains glittering at them, across the uplands wavering with heat. The thought of that coolness—sharp air for bursting lungs and snow for wrists and foreheads—was maddening when they let themselves dwell on it, yet every man-Jack realized clearly that in fact the mountains promised trouble and toil beside which this was easy going.

That was, unless there were help for them among the Indians there.

Daily they saw smoke columns on the horizon to the westward and on the flanks of their march.

"Those," Sacajawea said, "are signal fires of my people. They have seen you, without letting you find them."

She stood in the midst of the men, in her tattered deer-skin, proud with a regained membership in the tribe they approached as petitioners.

"They do not know who we are," she said. "They will have heard your guns, and think you must be Black-feet. So they set the prairie grass on fire and it is seen in all the mountains round about. The warriors will be ready."

Lewis, having understood, said, "The Great White Father does not wish us to give battle to your warriors. How shall we show them that we come in peace?"

"When you meet my people, give them the sign that among us means friendship. Spread a blanket on the ground. That is the sign. It means you wish to sit down and talk in peace."

"We shall carry a blanket always, when we scout ahead," said Lewis.

"If you come to a Shoshone camp," Sacajawea warned him, "you must never walk into it quietly. That is the way enemies come. As soon as you see any of my people, stand still and call out loudly."

Lewis nodded, watching her face while Charbonneau translated.

"If you meet women," Sacajawea said, talking beyond her husband, facing the mountains, remembering, "hold out your hand, and that will show them you wish them to lead you where they live."

Fatalist that he was, Lewis was swept by a shiver of exultation. Destiny, that had put this girl to wait for him at the Great Bend of the Missouri, must be his ally! All his dreams, all his plans, all his careful calculations, gone over and over with Jefferson, had itemized nowhere the single sheer stroke of luck on which all now depended.

"Tell your wife," he said to Charbonneau, with a smile and a warmth the trader had never seen on Monsieur Louis' face before, "that I am beginning to believe she is the good medicine of this entire expedition."

Yet once more they almost lost their luck. The blazing heat was brewing up its anger in the mountains. Thunderclouds came boiling and piling among the peaks and spread swiftly across the enormous sky. The cloudburst caught the party as it was strung out all along the portage. Some men, without shelter, were knocked to the ground by hailstones big as duck eggs. All were drenched, bruised, breathless and shivering, and precious goods were soaked to the core in a moment.

But Captain Clark, Pomp, Charbonneau and Sacajawea took refuge in a side canyon, under the slight shelter of an overhanging cliff. They were just congratulating themselves that the hail had ceased its pelting, when the heavens opened and in an instant the canyon floor was a flood. Then Sacajawea heard a sound that any western Indian understands and dreads—the mutter and boom of a wall of water suddenly let loose from above and sweeping down a narrow draw. She cried out to them, and pointed where she saw the water advancing. Charbonneau leaped at the cliff and scrambled up with an agility belonging to cats. Clark seized his rifle, and the Indian girl reached for the baby where she had laid him on the ground. She caught him up in her arms and was not even erect again before the flash flood swept away the papoose cradle and the very blankets on it. Clark's compass and notebooks went with it. The next instant the water was rising around their thighs, and Clark thrust the girl up the cliff just as she lost her footing.

"Charbonneau!" he shouted, above the tempest. "*Tenez*! *Tirez*! Here are your wife and child in danger!"

But the trader's rolling eyes watched only the torrent of death below him; he was once more paralyzed with fright. Pomp and Sacajawea would have been drowned if Clark had not found a giant's strength to hold them up until the flood subsided as quickly as it came.

"Gawd A'mighty, Mastuh Will'am," quavered York's voice then from the height above them. "Wheah's yo' at? Or is yo' daid?"

His master shouted reassurance. "Come down here, you black beggar, and help us out of this!"

The portage at last was done. The boats again were floated and loaded. But the *Experiment* had failed at last. With a frame of iron thirty-six feet long, four and a half feet wide, and two feet two inches deep, by Lewis's specifications, it had been coaxed and threatened, poled from behind and dragged from above, by human muscle and inhuman patience, from Pittsburg to above the

Great Falls, more than two thousand miles. Now it had sprung its seams for the last time, and there was no more pitch to mend it, and no more faith to sail it. It was buried, without honors, and in its place three frail canoes were shaped from warping cottonwood—of all worthless timber—and launched for the final reaches of the diminishing Missouri.

On July the fourth, the last of the "spiritous liquors" was served out to celebrate the glorious day. Again the two fiddles rejoiced, and on the wild green, amid flax flowers and harebells, the men tramped out an American reel. By plan prearranged with Jefferson, a small detachment of the party would have been sent east here from the foot of the Rockies with reports. But Lewis, watching the dancing men, couldn't find one he'd have the heart to turn back now.

Two years ago this day the news of the purchase of Louisiana had arrived in Washington; the cannon had told it. By the schedule drawn up in the White House, they should have been by this time at the Pacific, and ready to turn back. The men had guessed, from the fact that this was the last of the rum, how far out were the captains' calculations in point of time. But they saw with pride that their officers and the little squaw had not missed one right turning. The course was running true. Their blood ran with it, high and fiery tonight, as they tramped and stamped and sashayed. So, St. Louis, expect us when you see us! So, Pittsburg gals, Kentucky gals, you better not forget us! You'll know we're back when you're kissed from behind, and squeezed where you're soft, in the bargain. It may be long, but we'll be coming. We'll all be coming home, Long Tom, and we'll bring your captains with us.

☙ XIV

AGAIN THE BERRIES were ripe at the Three Forks of the Missouri. The chokecherries and currants and gooseberries, black and yellow and red, were juicily fat under a hot sun. Again it was high summer on the plateau at the foot of the Rockies, where the slow rivers meet beneath the cliffs. Again there were swallows taking the burnished air, and once more a mallard family had returned and chosen a site among the cattails for anchorage.

The cottonwoods were still aimlessly talking with their woman-tongued leaves; their down was scattered in tufts on the rosebushes and silvery buffalo-berries. Nothing had changed, in four years or four hundred.

Always summer comes back this way in this place; July returns with a breath warm as a buffalo's. And always like this the thunderheads come piling up from behind the Bitterroots. They rise like angelic announcement, their summits toppling in radiance, but their bellies hold the threat of storm, and they scud along, level with the vast level of the plain, in a tremendous, vaporous declamation of destiny.

The clouds of Montana, enormous as it is, diminish everything beneath them. They are more than the islands of the braided Missouri; their shadows troop across the high grass plain like the vanished herds. Their rain-haunted bases are dark as the band of conifers halfway up the mountainsides, and however high the snows shine, the clouds gleam higher.

Under the sky, under the clouds, under the nearing, slowly unfolding wall of the mountains, crept the little dark file of the expedition. The bighorns on the crags above the river watched them pass below, with uncomprehending yellow stare. To the sheep no rocky wall was any barrier; they clattered where, Lewis records with wistful admiration, it was manifestly impossible that any quadruped should stand. From her nest topping a lone tree above the triple falls, a she-eagle had watched the crawling portage, and when the men set forth again in their canoes up river, she soared ahead, screaming of their approach. All the way, in the days that followed, from the Great Falls to the Three Forks, the Indians for hundred of miles about had known that strangers were coming.

And the Indians had only to wait, to see what this party intended. They had the confidence of people on home ground, of aborigines who had never met the white man and knew only that certain good things came from him in barter. Everything here was supreme in its place, eagle and Indian, bighorn, and otter fishing the river that grew clearer with every upward mile. Nothing was needed here, nothing new had been looked for. The wide reaches of sun-dried grass, the deeply forested slopes, the snowy summits that gave the water-veins to all this land, sufficed themselves, in a vast and equable dimension.

But now came strange men—not, like the Indians, equal to this dimension, but superior to it. These were men with a view infinitely longer than any eagle's. Though they crawled at the bottom of the endless valley, they could see over the mountains where no pass was known to them, and behold the final horizon of the Pacific. They could hold in their heads, unmapped, a territory now comprising four states, which neither they nor any others before them had defined. Their thoughts ran with the rivers, from source to mouth, eastward or westward from the Great Divide. They read the land as they crossed it; they knew their way and where they were in relation to the entire globe, by the flickering compass and by the little shining brass quadrant in Lewis's box, with its sights and mirrors and graduated arc. To a nicety they daily took noon observations and regulated their watches thereby, so that even time was not lost for them, here where time had never mattered.

They read the rivers, volume, velocity, clarity, breadth. They read the vegetation, and when grass gave way to pines, and then spruce and fir appeared above the pines, they could foretell the climate they would meet. They did not fail to note the dusky grouse, the pinyon jay, the Lewis woodpecker, the Clark nutcracker, and describe them for science. These mountain birds, with screaming tongues or rapping bill or drumming, gave news among themselves of the newcomers, as they were talked about between the interested captains.

What went along with the men, ahead of them, ahead even of the vainglorious clouds forever storming on overhead, was purpose. It made no boast, threw back no light; it went the hard way, sure of itself and slow in the proof, mile by clogged and stubborn mile.

The Missouri river draws a long indenting finger of greenery across the tawny aridity of the plains. Thus it traced a foredestined path for the coming white men. It prepared the soft alluvial fields, where redwings whistle in the cattails and the pleasant marsh stink mingles with the scent of willow-herb and roses, for the plows that would follow where these canoes found the way. Eons ago, the river had cut a road between the limestone cliffs; always it led; shoal or rapid, it was the only path open. Day and night their ears were full of the sound of it, their clothes were heavy with it, and their thirst was slaked by it. Twinkling, racing, deepening, or faithlessly going shallow under their keels, or mad with stony white rapids, the Missouri was the sparkling vein that kept alive their hope.

At the Three Forks the captains judged that, all three streams here being of equal dimensions, the Missouri proper had come to an end and therefore they would name its confluences separately. The easternmost river they christened the Gallatin, for the Secretary of the

Treasury; the middle fork, which headed out of the mountains to the south, they called the Madison. But to the westernmost branch, whose headwaters Sacajawea told them that her people held, they gave the honor of the name of Jefferson. And this they determined to follow till they found the very spring where it arose.

The captains considered the Three Forks to be a spot crucial in the geography of the western hemisphere. They thought of it as almost the head of navigation of the whole Missouri river system. Lewis, from the top of the bluff where the swallows nested, on July twenty-seventh looked upon the three diverging rivers that ran to the rim of the land, on the rich land itself and on the ring of mountains, and felt as a man does who places his hand upon a thing and says, "This I have won."

Clark returned from a foray up the Jefferson feverish sick with what may have been a touch of dysentery, but fevered too with excitement.

Thus the two captains bent in eager creation over the map that day by day they were enlarging. Seasoned explorers that they were, they were not easily led to celebrating triumphs. Now they were elated; they felt that they had crossed a waste like purgatory, empty of even Indians. They had found at last a place which they had dared foresee; they had reached a point that was known intimately to the woman who guided them. For she had told them that it was from this very spot she had been ravished.

"You'll observe, Billy," remarked Lewis, in regard to

this, "that the squaw shows no emotion. Here is the place where she suffered violence, yet it appears to mean no more to her than anywhere else."

Clark said, "Poor child! Perhaps it pains her to remember."

Lewis nodded, but, "You'd think," he said, "she would be more happily excited at the prospect of soon meeting with her relations again."

"Are even civilized people," Clark laughed, "always so overjoyed at a reunion with their relations?"

Both men, so versed in topography, botany, zoölogy, navigation and astronomical observations, still could not read that round young Indian face. For here at the Three Forks, with the yellow currants in her palm, she tasted the fruit of pride again, and pride like this is too great to show. She did not dream that the white chiefs expected her to jump for glee; she couldn't have done it if they had asked her. When you let a bird free, it goes back to the trees, and at once it is a wild bird again, without thanks, regrets or sentiment. Here she was born, and here belonged; she was part of this Nature and could be nothing but natural in it. Did the trees weep for her when she was stolen from them? Or the mountains melt their hearts?

Now she returned from the wealth and the squalor of the alien Mandans, from the prairies with never a hill to lift the heart. Now she came back from her slavery, her concubinage, in triumph, to her home. She had been torn from it crying, a little maid stripped naked. She returned with jewels upon her breast, a child upon her back, a man-child that she had been a thousand miles and five years gone, to fetch here.

More, she wore honor in the eyes of great chiefs, white chiefs. They were so great she loved humility before them. You rivers, look on them. See how they are mighty. They say there is a nation coming behind them. And from here I shall lead these captains of a nation to the waters they are seeking.

Never would the white chiefs see her weak. Never should they say, among themselves, she is only a squaw forever talking; she is a child who cries; she is halt and slow and keeps us waiting.

So with Pomp on her back she went gathering berries, hard red serviceberries, chokecherries that it takes an Indian to swallow with a straight face, elderberries and currants. With these the captains could lace their venison. The rivers, like time, went by her, talking, glittering; the cottonwoods gossiped; the mallard family ventured out of port, quacking low in their throats.

"Yes, there she is gathering berries," agreed Billy Clark, looking up from his map-making, "as matter-of-fact as Scannon here. I suppose she does not feel all we feel, as you suggest. And we'd be wrong to expect it. She's another breed. But I've taken mightily to her, for all that."

"You've taken mightily to the baby, Billy," Lewis smiled. "And which one of us has not?"

"Who indeed?"

Pomp knew enough now to like things himself, and to be happy watching the world go by, from between his mother's shoulders. He saw the cottonwood fluff come floating down, and this vaguely amused him. When she turned, he saw the mallards paddling in the stream, with interest. He could look up, always, at the naked sky under which he had spent all his life, and its great brightness drew his baby heart to wonder. They were intelligent eyes, those dark halfbreed ones, and they were to see many and curious things in a world a continent and an ocean away from the Three Forks. He was to be intimate with princes of Europe. He, who could not yet say one word, would speak many languages. His destiny lay between the white men and his Indian mother; the stronger strain in him would in the end prevail.

Above the Three Forks the Jefferson river began to show what it could do. It could snag and ground the boats as though it had teeth in it; it spun them around and half filled them; it tripped and tumbled the men when they struggled in it, towing, and long before its hundred miles were run, it had lamed many of the party. One had an arm dislocated—that was Pryor; Pat Gass had strained his back. Charbonneau had sprained his ankle, and made the most of that. Drouillard hurt his leg and made the least of it. Another got a bad stone-bruise, too painful to set foot upon, and two had ugly inflammations in flesh worn with rubbing and toil. Nevertheless they were all eager as ever—eager, for one thing, to be done with the boats and commence the land journey.

The scenery, the men opined, must have been beautiful, but their eyes were full of sweat and gnats. Horseflies and mosquitoes attacked their bare backs, and their necks were of necessity ever bent forward, their gaze upon the channel or the trail. It was lined on each side, this winding corridor into the mountains, by a golden streak of beardgrass, the color of stubble wheat. There was tantalizing greenery of mountain spruce and alpine fir far above them, and beyond them the snowline floated serene and gleaming.

They remembered the valley of the Jefferson afterward not for its beauty but as the leg of the journey where the toil was hardest yet. Everyone would have given this kingdom for a horse. Long had the Shoshone mounts been horses of legend, and they gleamed like that in the imagination of the weary men. Once Clark saw a wild horse, standing alone far on the prairie, his head flung up to smell the new taint on his air. But at a hundred paces, when Clark approached, the beast began to trot, and when Clark quickened his pace, it showed him a burst of derisive speed.

There were horse tracks in a regular trail that sometimes came down to the river. Sacajawea nodded. "I know this trail," she said. "My people have many horses."

Again the hunting and scouting parties would strike such trails, and sometimes the tracks were very fresh, the droppings not yet dry. Yet where you could see miles and miles in the clear air, nothing moved but the grass under the passing of the wind.

It was a proof of the nearness of a powerful band of Indians that the game was scarce, and shy when it was sighted. The minimum food requirements of the thirty-two active persons on the expedition amounted to four deer a day, full-grown bucks or does, not fawns; or one deer and one good elk; or one buffalo. Besides this meat, there was constant need of elkskin for clothing and for moccasins. The river rocks, and the beardgrass and prickly-pear on land, wore out a pair of moccasins in two days. So no matter how tired the men were, they had had to work over the tough leather at every camp; now they prayed for the elk that would give them such employment.

The only plenteous animal was beaver. These little engineers had dammed the river and its tributaries throughout the whole course of the Jefferson. In the amplitude of wilderness time they had turned every watercourse till all twisted like snakes, and the rush and sedge, cattail and grass and wild iris had filled the older ponds until both sides of the river for a mile about looked like exquisite soft sward. But when you tried to walk across it, it was all bog, full of deep holes and quaking tussocks.

On a fine summer day, in the timeless course of his happy life, an old chief beaver wanders into American history. It all came about because Lewis, with his habitual impatience to see more, had gone ahead, scouted up one branch of a dubious fork and, finding the stream he chose to be unnavigable, had returned to the fork determined to warn Clark against it. So he penned a note to Billy, who would be coming in the boats, and posted it, if you please, on a shoot of willow. This was an established custom with the explorers; with so much space about and so few men in it, they show always a breathtaking confidence in finding each other again. When one of the party would be lost for days—and it happened over and over—another would start out, over trackless North America, calling the missing man's name on the hills, shooting off a gun and blowing Ordway's horn. They did not long wait for a laggard man; they pushed on, perhaps leaving him a note about where they had gone, like this one on the willow.

But it was a green shoot, and suitable to the old beaver's purpose. So he set his chisel teeth to it, quite unconcerned with the forward march of a nation, and in a very few industrious minutes, where there had been a growing sapling, there was now a stump. He dragged the willow length with practised skill into the junction of the Jefferson and the rapid stream just dubbed by Lewis the Wisdom, in honor of the President's loftiest attribute, and swam away with it on his own business. The note floated free, and the little ripples, lapping endlessly against the shore, worked it in time to sodden nothing.

So that lost the expedition many hours, for Clark chose the wrong fork too, and had to come back again to the junction.

When manifestly the Jefferson was not going to afford them many more miles of navigation, Lewis determined to go ahead and find the Indians who had the horses which now they must acquire. It was really Clark's turn to scout forward, and he was eager to go, but he was suffering with boils, so he shoved Lewis off with a clap on the shoulder.

"Speak pretty to the Shoshones when you find them, Meriwether. You've got to make them love you, though Lord knows why they should."

"I've got to get pack animals if I have to turn horse-thief to do it," Lewis grimly answered.

He chose to take with him Shields, because he was a crack shot and a quick thinker in a crisis, and Drouillard because he knew the Indian sign language and, a half-breed himself, could follow a trace long cold. McNeal he took because he was a long-legged rascal with enough enthusiasm to keep him leaping over barriers of fatigue.

And why, you ask, did he not take Sacajawea? He still knew too much and too little about her. He knew, that is, this much about every Indian squaw: that she has commonly no voice in council, and though he depended upon this girl to know the way and the language, he depended on himself alone to conquer the Shoshones by diplomatic authority. He was determined now to overtake the Indians wherever they fled him or avoided him, and he could not be burdened, he supposed, with a woman and her infant.

So he left her, his lucky piece, behind with the boats that were toiling so slowly now that half a mile an hour was good speed.

Philanthropy was the name that Lewis gave to the east fork of the Jefferson, which he encountered as he went striding on over the golden hills, for that was the sweetest of the President's attributes. Lewis took the west fork to be the way to the Lemhi Shoshones; when he left a note this time, he put it on a dry old willow pole such as a beaver would not choose. For this was a message Clark must not miss; in it his fellow captain told him that neither fork was navigable and that therefore the party with the boats was to wait here at the junction. Then Lewis strode on; he had an Indian trace under his feet, and he was feeling the surer of himself the closer he got to the point where all he had accomplished so far must fail or be forwarded.

So he pressed on with his heart quick and light, though the burden on his back must have been heavy. For it consisted in his blanket, a load of dry meat and flour, presents for the Indians of mirrors, beads, moccasins and paint, as well as a store of powder and lead for bullets. Add to this his telescope, his journal and writing materials, and the gun he bore, and here you have civilization walking self-sufficient into the wild.

On the third day Lewis lost the Indian trail. With his eye he measured the breadth of the valley floor between the cliffs. The fine sweet valley was only about a mile wide, he considered. So that it shouldn't, he was sure, be hard to strike the trace again, and he deployed his little party to cover the valley for sign. Drouillard he sent off to his left and Shields to the right. He kept McNeal beside him, because you never could tell what would become of that boy if you weren't watching him. If anyone saw Indian sign, he was to raise his hat on the muzzle of his gun. But after a march of five miles up the long narrow valley, there was still no signal from either side.

Then, far ahead, Lewis made out a tall and moving object. He shot out his telescope and put it to his eye. In the circle of the lens there moved toward him a solitary Indian horseman. He was, Lewis intently perceived, a man of no nation as yet familiar. For arms this savage warrior carried a bow and a quiver of arrows, and he rode a splendid horse without saddle, with a cord for bridle.

The white man and the red horseman approached each other without slackening pace, but they were still nearly a mile apart when the Indian must have seen Drouillard and Shields moving up on the flanks of his advance. No Shoshone is caught by a stratagem so simple as this appeared to be, and Lewis in his glass found that his quarry had reined in to a halt.

To his companion he muttered, "Why the devil don't those two fools stand still and let him come on to me?"

"Give them a signal, Captain," suggested the cheery McNeal.

"If I do, the Indian will misread it and gallop off, no doubt. It's their accursed curiosity that drives our men on to him. Well, I feel it myself," he admitted. "Let's hope the Shoshone has his share."

Swiftly he undid his pack, opened out the blanket, and catching it by the corners he waved it over his head and spread it on the ground as invitation to powwow. Three times he made this sign of friendship that Sacajawea had taught to him. Then he whirled bright beads around his head, and with a mirror caught the sun and flashed it toward the brave. At last he picked up the blanket and leaving his gun behind with McNeal, walked slowly across the wild meadow toward the stationary horseman.

"*Tabba bone! Tabba bone!*" he called in a ringing shout, and he rolled his sleeves up to the elbows and bared his chest, to show how white his mother had borne him.

But the Indian looked over his left shoulder and then his right. Lewis saw him pick up the bridle. Desperate now, the captain made a signal to Shields and Drouillard to stop their flanking advance; the halfbreed at least observed it and obeyed. But just as Lewis had feared, the Shoshone took it for the signal to attack, wheeled his horse, galloped toward the mountains, and swiftly had vanished.

The keenness of Lewis's disappointment was as sharp as his anticipation had been. For a moment he swore like a gentleman; then, as his men came up, he shut himself up like his own telescope.

"Well, Shields," he did permit himself to say with that quiet acerbity that ate into a man, "I wouldn't have expected it would be you who spoiled our hopes. You, Drouillard, I would have hoped knew more of Indians than to let one think you were attempting to surround him. Both of you lost your heads and a chance of success for the expedition."

The men took their reproof like soldiers and McNeal swallowed a grin.

"I catch him," promised Drouillard fervently. "I track him."

"Here, McNeal," Lewis ordered. "Cut me a pole there by the river. We'll raise our colors, at least."

For this man who was advancing accoutered with the necessities of civilization had not forgotten to bring too its finest emblem. So the American flag was borne up Shoshone Cove, as they named it, and up the first slopes of the Rocky Mountains, on August eleventh, 1805, in the proud hands of young Hugh McNeal.

❧ XV

MERIWETHER LEWIS awoke at day-break next morning, in his camp at the foot of the Great Divide, to a world silvered with night frost upon the sagebrush, and to the conviction that before dusk fell he would have tasted, in this one day, the headwaters of the eastward flowing Missouri, and those of the Columbia rolling to the Pacific. The thought reached his mind like a blast of reveille while sleep still clung to him, so that he was on his feet in a moment, wide awake, stretching cold limbs and flailing them against his chest. He looked down the length of Shoshone Cove that he had come, and drew in the sharp, empty air between his teeth with a whistle of satisfaction. McNeal was still awake on sentry duty, pacing druggedly up and down at some distance from the campfire; he caught sight of his captain and saluted him good morning cheerily.

"Have you heard or seen anything, McNeal?"

"No Indians, and no breakfast. Unless you'd have wanted to eat owl."

"We haven't quite come to that, though provision is low and the game looks scarcer, doesn't it, with every mile." Lewis stepped over to Drouillard, and shook the sleeping hunter's shoulder kindly. "Wake up, now, man! We're needing you and your gun."

Then he roused Shields. "This is the day," he said to them all, smiling. "This is going to be the great day."

Hugh McNeal, rubbing the chill off his hands, cut a caper to warm his heels too. "We're going to sprinkle salt on the tails of those Shoshones, eh, Captain?"

They started on up the cove that steadily narrowed to the west and mounted; in a few miles, after passing some abandoned stick-lodges, Drouillard, the trail-finder, fell in with a clear Indian path. So they felt they could halt now, and make a breakfast on the last of their venison. With nothing but a piece of jerk and some flour in reserve, they were in a gambling frame of mind to risk all on a great future.

A year and a half ago Lewis had launched his pirogues and canoes upon the mighty Missouri where it poured out in a dirty flood into the Mississippi. Now he had followed this gigantic river system to its westernmost reaches. It went beside him here, a very baby of a stream. This river that had borne his iron boat, his canoes, all his party, now could carry no more than a petal or a leaf. The coffee-colored flood had become a rivulet of purest, coldest spring water. And just before it vanished wholly into the mountainside, the vainglory in McNeal burst forth in a bound. He crashed down through the rushes and cornel along the brook, and with a leap he planted one foot on each side of the water and shouted, "Thank God I've lived to straddle the Missouri!"

Lewis laughed, with the rest of them. "Thank God for all of us," he agreed devoutly, "that we are halfway to the Pacific, and a quarter of the whole way home."

He was like that, Shields thought; he was always just, even to the Lord when he praised Him. He seemed, as a captain, to be sure of winning out, but he made you feel that every success chiefly depended on you alone. He hinted always that the next thing would be harder, and it mostly always was. And you trusted him, just as you never expected to be let off. Newman, who had talked mutiny on the way from St. Louis to Fort Mandan, had taken his stripes for it with courage enough to make a hero of him. For months he had tried to win his way back into the party. But it wasn't any use. When Captain Lewis lost faith in you, you were done. When he forgave you, it was as completely. After Willard fell asleep at his sentry post and was properly punished for it, there wasn't a thought of it ever to be seen in the captain's eyes again. Captain Lewis, Shields reflected, was worse than a man's own conscience, and yet he was kinder.

To Lewis this seemed to be the morning for which he had lived all his thirty-one years. Here where the spring that would become Missouri gushed from the rock under lodgepole pines and firs, he laid down his pack at last with a sigh of exultation, and threw himself on his back

187

on the resinous dry needles. The Rockies were beneath him, upholding his body; the western sky arched warm and blue above him, and his hand played in the icy rill.

And why should they not halt a minute, having pressed thus far? The day was not old yet, and here, Lewis knew, just here he would never stand again. Raised a country lad, trained a soldier, he had, when he was setting a pole in the river with the rest of the men, when he shouldered a pack, when he tracked a deer or retreated from a bear, all a frontiersman's hickory-bough strength, so that he could throw himself into outward life with the stoutest. But by temperament he was a man who lived inwardly. Nothing ever happened to him without his realizing it. What he could enjoy he savored with tastes perfected by civilized education, and with a peculiar understanding of the significance of each experience, personal and historic. Now in this instant his outward self and his inner were in absolute balance. His body rejoiced in its rest; his mind relished the thought that these great fir trees, much darker and more beautiful than any he had ever seen before, must have stood here, to judge by their boles, for three or four hundred years at least. They would have been growing when Columbus raised the Bahamas from the west. They were strong when Jamestown was founded; they were venerable when the United States was born, in blood and fire. But now at last the flag had caught up with them!

Lewis got to his feet. "Well, men, on we go. This was

a goal to us; now we must put it behind us, and push on to the next."

So the flag was borne up the last eastward slope of the Divide, through mountain meadows where the mariposa lilies blew, frail cups holding the sunshine and spilling it out again into the wind when it tossed them. Indian paintbrush daubed the long grass with vermilion, and the first asters to hint of autumn were opening where the summer yarrow faded. The startled birds of the Lemhi pass parted at the sight of the fluttering bright standard. The sage hens scudded low away over the silver brush, clucking in alarm; flickers showed white tails of retreat as they sailed for the pines up on the ridge. The crows called a warning that was answered by other such sentries from dead tree to tree, and overhead Lewis saw two great black hawks that waited grandly on above the marching colors, and westward took their soaring way.

Then the four climbing men reached finally the back-bone of this continent and stood there, panting, staring. Range upon blue range, the stony billows of the Rockies rolled beyond them, in a sea of relentless distance. The men had been coming westward for three thousand miles, but only now they saw the ultimate West, the grand sunsetward slope of the far side of this vast water-shed. It rolled away and away surging up in piled reaches without limit, a challenge, a defiance, a promise. In the silence, upon its pole, the flag of the United States rippled out with an answering murmur.

Lewis tore his eyes away. Time enough to gloat over the glory of all that space when he had conquered it. He was as eager now to find the first westward flowing water as McNeal had been to straddle the Missouri. Not to be forestalled, he hastened ahead of the men, as if this were all a boy's adventure. His practised eye caught the wandering fringe of leafy bushes that meant a stream course, and he broke from the Indian path through the high flowered grass and leaped down the slope to the spot where it seemed to begin.

There it was, the pure spring bubbling out of the mountainside and promptly setting its course for the west. Lewis dropped to his knees beside it, put his hands on the cold rocks of its basin, set his lips to it and drank deeply.

Here, he writes, *I first tasted of the water of the Great Columbia River.*

Then they went on down, from this moment of hard-won glory. Steeply they descended into a profound valley forested with the first great stand of trees that had marched to meet them. It greeted them with the coolness of ancient damp and shadow, the breath of ferns and resin and cold wet rock. It had a voice, too, the steady rushing sound of gathering waters and of wind perpetually plowing through needled boughs. The larkspur stood lance-high, brilliant blue in the gloom of the conifers, and the mock-orange bush shone out a starry white.

That night, having procured no game all day, they ate

the last of their dried meat, and for the first time slept upon pine boughs with the aromatic breath of them in their nostrils.

Day was only a promise in the sky when Lewis was up once more, calling the others awake. Five miles from their camp they came out of the mountain forest into a rolling plain, and there, in full view before them, stood two Indian women, a man, and a pack of barking dogs.

The Shoshones watched, minutely attentive, the slow advance of the white men. Lewis had unfurled the flag again; now, when he could be heard, he cried "*Tabba bone!*" while he showed his white upper arm and waved bright beads enticingly. But as soon as he came near, the little party broke like a herd of antelope, and fled over the hill and out of sight.

"After them, men!" cried Lewis. "This time we've got to catch them."

And the white men pounded over the hill and into the next ravine. There the Shoshone man was nowhere to be seen, and instead of two Indian women there were now three, a young one, an old one, and a little girl. The young squaw turned and ran away with loping gait, but the grandmother and the child, despairing of all safety, sat down on the ground, bowed their shoulders, and stretched forth their necks to await the death blow of the enemy.

Captain Lewis dropped his rifle on the ground, advanced to this pathetic pair and gently took the old woman's brown claw in his. She looked up at him with filmy eyes and he saw surprised relief sweep over her walnut-brown wrinkled face.

Drouillard and Shields came up at his summons, and from their packs Lewis took out a pewter mirror and a little vermilion paint. These he gave to the grandmother, talking all the time in a voice that would reassure any animal thing. Then he found a short string of beads and put it over the little girl's head. The red baubles glittered on her flat bronze breast and she looked up at him with her black eyes blank with awe.

He patted the child's round sleek head. "So you see, Granny, we come as friends," he finished.

The old woman answered in Shoshone—what, he did not know.

"Tell this woman, Drouillard, as best you can, to go and find that young squaw who is hiding. Because we wish her to lead us to the chiefs of the Shoshones. And we will give her many beads and mirrors."

The halfbreed could talk the sign language almost as fast as a man can move his tongue. It was a common medium of communication that enabled redskins to understand each other though their languages differed as much as English, Chinese, and Hebrew. The old woman, deeply impressed and breathless with excitement, humped away over the hill, while the little girl stood staring at Lewis, trembling but courageous and transfixed with curiosity.

McNeal came up and squatted on his heels before her. "My, my!" he pretended to marvel. "Where'd you get those rubies?" And he lifted the string on a finger and grinned up at her his mischievous warm grin.

Any age or color, thought Shields dryly, petticoats or none, so long as it's women, for Hugh.

The young squaw came back, breathing hard; her fluttering heart would scarce supply her lungs. But there was no resisting, to a people so immemorially enslaved to magic, the lure of these bright mysteries. So she stood still, trembling only a little, while Captain Lewis gravely painted her cheeks with vermilion, which was, Sacajawea had taught him, emblematic of peace among her people. Then he painted the old woman and even the little girl and, holding out his hand to the young squaw, he said, in Shoshone, "Lead me."

They had not gone two miles down the river when around a curve of the trail came swinging a troop of about sixty mounted warriors. They rode with the reckless ease and speed of men who go so little afoot they are one with their horses; they came on at a dash, dark faces set, the fringes and tails of their skin dress flying back from the centaur torsos.

Lewis laid down his gun, motioned to his men not to move, and advanced bearing the flag. The chief and two headmen, splendid with fur and shell and porcupine quill adornment, rode out to the fore of the troop and reined in sharply beside him.

The Indian women, commanded by Lewis, hurried up, and the chief in a dark voice demanded to know, as Lewis plainly made out, who were these strangers advancing into the tribal hunting-grounds? The women made eager answer, exultingly showing off the presents they had been given. The three magnificent Shoshone headmen at once threw themselves off their horses, and embraced Lewis cordially in the Shoshone fashion. A wave of bear's grease and Indian stink swept over him, together with relief, as each threw an arm around his shoulder and pressed a hard cheek to his, crying, "*Ah hi e, ah hi e!*" "I am much pleased! I am much rejoiced!"

The whole troop now quit their horses and suffocated the Americans with these brotherly embraces, leaving paint and grease upon the stiffly smiling white faces.

"Whew!" remarked the irrepressible McNeal beneath his breath to Shields, "sweet as skunks, ain't they?"

"They say skunk too is mighty friendly, if you ever dared find it out," Shields answered.

The captain, tucking back a smile, warned, "Everything, men, depends on your behavior now. Don't alarm any of them, and for God's sake don't give offense. Keep your mind on those handsome horses we've got to have, and your eyes on the barter stuff. They don't love us like this for ourselves alone, you know."

Lewis knew his Indian ceremonies; when the Shoshones seated themselves in a circle, he understood that it was for him to fill the pipe and pass it around. So he lit the calumet, blew a whiff into the air, and offered the pipe solemnly to the chief. But before this dignitary accepted it, he must first pull off his moccasins, a sign,

Sacajawea had explained, that should he ever break friendship now he hopes he may go barefoot forever.

Then Lewis, his throat tortured with thirst, hunger in his belly, and sweat in his eyes, summoned himself to make as ceremonious an address as, with Drouillard's help, he could. He came, he said, in peace, and as a symbol of that peace he would give his flag to the chief. He came asking the help of the great Shoshone people, and how they might help him he would explain, if they would lead him to their camp where he could talk at rest.

Translated by Drouillard, the reply of the tall Shoshone went thus: "I am the chief. My name is Cameahwait. We welcome you among us as brothers. We are glad to see the presents you have given our women. We hope you have more. Come with us and we will trade with you. We will take you to our camp and you shall rest there."

So they set off in fine marching order. The chief and headmen rode out first, pacing their horses with slow dignity. Behind strode the four white men, and after them came the rest of the troop, the horses' heads bowing restlessly to their pacing gait, and the red riders, at arrogant ease upon their Spanish mounts, looking as wild as the beasts whose hides dressed them. Their loose-fitting shirts and leggings were rich with fringe and porcupine quill and the dangling tails and split hoofs left on the antelope hides. Some of the men wore hide robes as well, dressed with the hair on, and many boasted tippets of finest fur, or the wings or tails of birds in their forelocks. An animal wealth hung upon the band, and yet all the faces had a hungry look, in itself fiercely animal.

They reached the spot elected by the chief for council. Soft antelope skins were spread upon green boughs, where the warriors pulled up the grass to light a little council fire. Dismounted, all the men stripped off their moccasins, and the white men, austere in their worn American clothes, stripped off their own in answering pledge of friendship. Then Cameahwait lighted his beautiful oval pipe of transparent green stone at the fire, puffed it, and blew smoke to the four corners of the world, beginning with the East and ending with the North. All the time he was speaking, while he thrice repeated this ceremony, like one who performs a solemn ritual, who takes his oath, and makes binding promises.

He was a lean man, taller than the rest, bony with high cheekbones and hard jaw, and it was his fierce clear eyes that made him look the leader, Lewis thought, even more than his dress. This was superb; over his elkskin shirt, opulently fringed and worked with quills in many colors, a buffalo robe fell royally from the shoulders; the fringe of his leggings was the richer for scalp-locks and dragged magnificently at his heels, and even his moccasins trailed skunk-tails. But the finest peltries were those that made his tippet, a collar falling nearly to the waist, made out of otter fur and ermine and set with gleaming pearl shells. Upon this lay a necklace of bear claws, and an eagle feather was thrust in his forelock.

Lewis sat gazing up at him, impressed by his bearing and his voice and the look of race in his savagery. Though Lewis could not understand the words Cameahwait spoke, the orator still made the white chief feel their beauty, their natural religious fervor. And it swept over Lewis that, while he had left behind the thousand-mile loneliness of the no-man's land that was the Great Plains, and come at last among fellow men who greeted him like brothers, nevertheless he had lost his pure freedom; he was surrounded; he sat now a guest, perhaps a prisoner, of a proud people who did not know this land was not still theirs.

When it was his turn to speak, Lewis arose and distributed the last of the presents he had brought. Then he explained that he and his men had been without food for many hours, and Cameahwait replied, without embarrassment, that unfortunately there was nothing at hand but berries—some serviceberries made into cakes and chokecherries dried in the sun. They brought Lewis also a small piece of fish, and when he saw the firm pink meat of it he knew, though he had never seen salmon before, that here was the famed monarch of Columbian waters. Therefore he could be confident that truly this way led toward the western sea.

He spoke of this to Cameahwait, to confirm the salmon's evidence.

197

"Yes," the chief told him through Drouillard, "this river here, which is the Lemhi, flows in half a day's march into the Salmon. But that we call the River of No Returning, for no one has ever got through its whirl-pools and waterfalls where it cuts a deep canyon in the mountains. The walls come right to the water; they are very high and steep. You cannot portage over the mountains there. You must not follow the Salmon river."

"How then must we go?"

Cameawhait stared at him opaquely through a wraith of camp smoke that blew between them. "The white chief wishes to go where?" he asked.

"I am on my way to the great water into which all rivers flow, far to the west."

"We call that, among us, the Big Stinking Water. It smells very bad, I have heard, of salt and dead fish." The black eyes were unflinching, inexpressive. "Why do not our brothers remain among us forever and be happy?"

"Tell him, Drouillard," directed Lewis, concealing his extreme weariness, "that the great chief of the white men in the East wishes to send this scouting party to the western waters, and he looks to the Shoshones to help him."

"Tell my brother," answered Cameahwait through the halfbreed, "that we have promised to help him, and we will not fail. We will show him the way. We will sell him horses as he has asked. But we can talk of all that tomorrow," he concluded, rising. "Now we are too happy to think of these things. For all the Shoshones wish to dance in honor of the white traders."

Lewis saw what was coming, but there was no way out of it, and he smothered his sigh. Presently, seated on antelope robes in state beside Cameahwait, he looked on, with the impassive approval he knew was expected of him, while the entire Lemhi band, braves, squaws and children, milled about, pushed close to stare into his face, or slapped their native earth with dancing feet to the heavy beating of the drum that kept up hour after hour. Lewis's head throbbed with it, and the women in the background raised an endless chant that they could keep up as katydids can. The men burst into yells at intervals; sometimes a single brave would go yipping about the camp, and again a chorus of them would deafen the night with wildcat cries of celebration.

At midnight Lewis stretched aching limbs and arose. Flesh could endure no more, and he explained to Cameahwait the fatigues of this day's march. So he was suffered to depart, as a privileged guest, but the rejoicing in his honor did not cease because he had retired. At the lowest it was an uproar, and twice in his sudden and heavy sleep Lewis was wakened by splitting orgiastic bursts of savagery.

❦ XVI

THE GREAT Shoshone nation held sway from Montana to northern Mexico, from California to Colorado. It is a family of Indians linked together chiefly by language. This does not mean that they all spoke the same language; their tongues were no closer together than Dutch and German, English and Norwegian, Flemish and Swedish, which are all in the Teutonic family. Very distantly, perhaps, the Shoshones are a branch of the great Aztec group. Shoshones had in common, too, the stern fate of having been thrust into or born in the desert or the mountains. Their enemies, the Blackfeet and Sioux, the Cheyennes and Minnetarees, drove them back from the buffalo plains in an endless warfare. The Pacific Coast tribes were also leagued against the Shoshones of the interior, keeping for themselves the salt and salmon of the big waters.

So the Shoshones were found on poor lands. They lived at the head of the salmon run, on the extreme edge of the buffalo range. Because the forage was poor in the mountains, they could count on few elk and deer. The Lemhi band could not raise even tobacco, but must buy it. They would travel a hundred miles to dig a few roots of the camas, the wild hyacinth.

Like most people shaped by a rocky environment, the Lemhi were tough and enduring, if they survived at all. They had a mountain pride and clannishness. They were touchy and, in their own fastnesses, fanatically courageous; correspondingly, they were easily dazzled by wealth, easily confused away from home. Mounted as they were, they had all the sense of superiority that the horseman feels above a man who walks. Their poverty was their boast and shame, and they were the fiercer for their habitual hunger.

Where the times were lean so long, and men or families must scatter so widely to forage, every man was something of a chief unto himself. There could be little interdependence among such people; there was too little wealth to make inheritance loom large among them. So that the chief of the band was not necessarily the son of the old chief, but rather that individual among them whose intelligence, personality and oratory made others look to him as leader. Such a man was Cameahwait.

He was the commander now of a tribe decimated by war, but unbroken in spirit. Most of the men had their coarse black hair cut short in the neck, in sign of mourning, for every family had lost warriors, and a hard grief, blent with stolidly borne hunger, made the atmosphere of the camp relentless, on the morning after the unbridled celebration. White men and red put thought of food before the desire for parley, so Cameahwait commanded an antelope surround to be performed in the valley below the camp. There a small herd was grazing, and twenty Indians armed with bows and arrows rode their Spanish-bridled horses out to encircle them.

The little springing beasts were fleeter than any horse foaled, but as the herd scattered the Shoshones closed in on it, one horseman relaying another in the pursuit of the escaping game. At full speed down steep ravines and up over hills the sure-footed horses dashed, chasing the antelope from one side of the encircled valley to the other. Soon the horses were heaving and lathered, but their light-footed prey seemed no more winded than the wind itself, and in the end every one of them showed nimble heels to the hoofs pounding after them, and vanished each in a high streak of dust.

"Goodbye, dinner!" said Shields to McNeal, turning away from the spectacle.

"That was breakfast and last night's supper too," replied McNeal aggrievedly.

Cameahwait was embarrassed but apparently not surprised at the result of the chase.

"It is the finest animal in the world," he explained, "with the best flesh and the softest skin. But it is also a very bad animal. Forty warriors may hunt all day, and the antelope will only let them catch two or three."

"Now it will be my pleasure," Lewis told his host, "to give you some of the white man's food."

And he mixed some of his last flour with water and currants and serviceberries and set to baking this into a cake. There was precious little of the flour left, and Cameahwait saw this.

"The white chief is generous," he said. "He shares what he has with his brothers. So we know he is a good man."

"You must wait and see if you like it," Lewis bantered lightly, squatting over the hot coals.

It was incredible to Lewis to see how fast Drouillard could knock such speeches out in sign talk. The halfbreed showed his two selves at such a time; you could see him go all Indian as he talked without speaking to Cameahwait, his mumness matching his immobile face and his hands flickering out symbols. Then when he turned back to Lewis he was all the white private again, attentive, obedient.

Cameahwait talked while he made the signs; he wished to be affable; he conveyed something by his voice as well as his gestures, and Lewis watched his face intently and listened to the words. Years ago, when he was just a young soldier stationed in Tennessee, with this day only a secret hope in his heart, he had set himself to learn the Chickasaw language and customs and to understand their thinking and diplomacy. Now it all stood him in good stead. So did his close study of the Mandans, and above all the hours he had spent with Sacajawea as her pupil.

By the time the little cake was baked, he had mastered many more words and phrases of the Shoshone tongue. He broke the hot bread ceremoniously, and gave Cameahwait half. The gaunt tall redman bit into it with solemn curiosity, and a smile of delight unlimbered his features.

"*Sa'i!*" he pronounced. "Good, very good, my brother!"

He took a pinch of the uncooked flour in his fingers and worked it curiously there, tasting with his tongue. "Is this a powdered root?"

"No," Lewis told him, "it is the seed of a grass. We call it wheat. The white men have it in the East."

"Do your squaws grow very much of this good seed?"

Lewis looked past his host eastward across the dusty valley where the antelope had vanished and horse and rider had sweated in vain, at the wall of the Bitterroots where the sharp spearpoints of the conifers outlined each unrelenting ridge, and he thought of the sagebrush plains beyond, of the cruel barbed beardgrass and the miles of prickly-pear; he remembered the hardwood wilderness of the Ohio valley, and the first outpost settlements whose ragged patches of cultivation held nothing better than Indian corn. Past all this went his mind, to the wheatfields of Maryland and Pennsylvania and Virginia; he could see the close gold of them, low and heavy and blowing all one way, and how they were pied, in the uplands, with fields of blue flax, red clover and lush timothy. He remembered the way it feels to a country boy to draw the harsh and freighted heads through the fingers, to split the fat kernels open, and taste the soul of bread raw on the tongue. The song of the reapers, the clash of the scythes, the golden cloud of chaff at threshing, the thundering complaint of the millstones, and the white dust on the old mill beams— how could you tell of them to this waiting savage?

He measured his answer, as he had learned to do, not in direct reply so much as to lead the conversation where, for his purposes, he needed it to go.

"Yes, we have much wheat, and many other good seeds. We have beads and knives, and plenty of paint and mirrors, in the East. My brother, who has red hair and is a great chief also, is coming up the Missouri river bringing such things in his canoes. But they cannot go very fast. As you know, the river is small and rapid there. What we need now is plenty of your fine horses, to go down to the river and meet my brother Redhead."

"We have the finest horses," replied Cameahwait. "If my white brother wishes to buy them, I will ask my people to sell him some."

Lewis saw that Cameahwait was now driving a bargain, and he went on carefully. "You have seen that I have given all my presents to you. I have shared my food with you like a brother. So I cannot buy the horses until the barter is brought here. It is very heavy because it is so much and so rich. If you will come to the river with me, with plenty of horses and your best braves, my men will leave their canoes and come here with all our goods."

Cameahwait answered, "I shall have to ask my braves. They own the horses. They do not have to come unless they wish to."

"If they will come," Lewis promised, "they will all be paid for their trouble." His tired mind whipped itself up. "And I must tell you that we have with us a Shoshone woman, one that was stolen away from here a long time ago, and she is coming back to visit you."

Cameahwait's face was enigmatic as ever. "I would like to see this squaw," he answered.

"Oh, yes," said Lewis to Drouillard, "and tell him about York. Say how big he is and how black, and about his kinky hair."

Word of this last miracle spread rapidly through the Shoshone camp, and McNeal soon came up grinning to his captain. "Drouillard says they're all mighty keen to see the nigger," he reported. "York's fetched 'em, and the horses along with 'em."

The commotion of departure appeared to be a very important part of the journey itself. Lewis could not see why they should not simply mount and leave, but nobody intended to forego the ceremony of setting forth. So that had to be celebrated, until everyone fell asleep exhausted.

And the next day everybody had cooled off.

Cameahwait dutifully harangued his warriors twice, but nobody now wanted to go. Then Lewis began to gather, from the chief's hints and looks and the words of Shoshone he caught, and by the glum and suspicious glances that were cast upon him, that his magic for these fickle people had worn off. Perhaps one of them had had a dream in the night, or a vision induced by so long a fast, or two squaws had talked until they believed each other. At any rate, the rumor was running that the white men were really agents of the Pah-kes, the bitterest enemies of the tribe. It was being said, Drouillard informed Lewis, that no sensible person could believe that there was a man with red hair anywhere, or one with skin black all over. And these presents that Lewis had given so freely were plainly nothing but a bait, to lure the honest Shoshones out onto the plain, where the Pah-kes would kill them and ride off on their horses.

Lewis swallowed down despair. In truth, he had nothing else to swallow, unless it were river water. He was faint with hunger and aching in all his limbs as a man will do when he once halts a forced march. The whole success of the expedition now trembled in the unstable balance of these savage children's favor. His immediate resources were exhausted, and furthermore he perceived that, if by any ill chance there should happen to be some Pah-ke war party roving the neighborhood, the Shoshones would be confirmed in their worst suspicions, and all the white men would pay with their lives.

Shields, Drouillard, and McNeal were watching him with covert anxiety. "It all goes to show you can't ever trust an Indian," Shields offered.

207

"Kiss you to smotheration one day," McNeal commented, "and lift your hair the next."

"It won't come to that," said Lewis quietly, "but watch what you say even in English, boys, because Indians are very acute. They understand the voice, the eyes." He knew that his own three men were intent upon his voice, his eyes, and he kept these steady, and smiled. "I'm not even blaming the Shoshones, you know. They're only right to suspect everybody. But I think I know how to touch them on their pride. Come, Drouillard."

He strode to Cameahwait, bracing his tired frame to the carriage of a commander. "Your people do not trust me," he challenged, staring Cameahwait in the eyes. "I know you trust me because we have shared bread like brothers. You are a chief, and therefore you have honor. I am also a chief and I do not lie to you." He paused a moment while Drouillard's quick hands made clear his meaning to the impassive Shoshone. "But you will have to tell your braves," Lewis then went on, "that I shall return to the canoes and tell the white traders to take their goods away again because the Lemhi band is a mean people, and afraid even to come forth to trade. Then no white traders will ever come this way again. Instead they will take their presents and their barter to other Indians, to your enemies, and make them strong."

Cameahwait was just visibly moved by this stinging speech. "Perhaps there are some people in my tribe," he admitted, "who are suspicious. I do not think as they do, and the best of my braves do not. We are not afraid of the Pah-kes or anyone else."

"Very well, then," answered Lewis. "If there are still some Shoshones who are not afraid, let them at once mount their horses and come with me. I will take them over the pass and down to the forks of the Missouri, and there my brother the Redhead will be waiting for me, and he will make everyone who is my friend rich."

Cameahwait mounted his horse before haranguing the tribe again. Only eight warriors accepted his challenge, but Lewis did not wait for any further changes in temper. Each white man mounted behind an Indian, the little cavalcade set forth, while behind them squaws wept and screamed, sang funeral dirges and prayed to their gods to preserve their men from certain destruction.

Yet before they had reached the top of the Lemhi pass, the troop was overtaken by the whole tribe. Everybody had plucked up reluctant courage, nobody wanted to be left out of the bargain and, the thought of black York having revived in their imaginations, all were eager for unimaginable wonders.

So Meriwether Lewis, a little white around the smiling lips, again lit the pipe of peace, while the horses grazed amid the mariposa lilies and the wind went wandering, indifferent to this ultimate clash between East and West at the height of the Divide, through the boughs of the lodgepole pines. The whole party made camp that night at the head of Shoshone Cove, and Lewis slept the sleep of the famished and the suddenly saved.

But the next morning, when he proposed to send two of his hunters out for food, the Indians saw through this stratagem immediately. Obviously, Drouillard and Shields were to go down and tell the Pah-kes that the game was now in the trap, and they could spring the ambush and slaughter all. So now most of the tribe began to stream back over the pass again, leaving only twenty-eight warriors and three women with Cameahwait.

"What do you make of the chief, Captain?" McNeal ventured to ask Lewis, crowding down tobacco into the bowl of his pipe, in place of breakfast. "What side do you reckon he's playing on?"

"I think he still trusts us," Lewis opined, considering. "And some of his men either trust us, or they are not afraid of anything they think we can do to them. But I can only say that if our party isn't at the foot of the cove when we get there, our goose may very well be cooked. Captain Clark has only to fail to see the note we left him at the forks, and continue up the wrong branch, away from us, to convince the Indians we are liars." He turned to this bold boy who put such faith in him, and smiled his level-eyed smile. "But when has Captain Clark failed?"

The warriors, who had gone suspiciously out with Shields and Drouillard when the white men went hunting, had not been absent an hour when one came galloping back, larruping his horse like mad, and yelling Lewis knew not what. The captain sprang onto the back of the nearest mount. If it's Pah-kes, he thought, we are done for. If it's Billy, we're saved.

But no one could or would tell him. All he knew was that the whole company, when they heard what the panting brave said, leaped on their horses. The wild horse Lewis sat bolted with the rest; he was jolted on the sharp bones of the beast till his teeth clattered; he sawed on the bridle, reining his mount in; he shouted, in Shoshone, French, and English, to find out what the cause of this stampede might be.

An Indian who leaped onto the horse's rump behind him had certainly something very definite in view, for he whipped the beast as hard on the flank as Lewis tugged at the bridle.

What the white captain beheld down the cove was the carcass of a deer lying amid the sage; beside it knelt Drouillard, and his knife flashed deftly. But before the halfbreed could cut steaks out of it, the Indians, dismounting, had thrown themselves upon the dead animal and were devouring all the offal that Drouillard had flung aside. Yet with savage honesty, they made no motion to lay hold on that part of the steaming carcass that the white man's knife marked out as his own.

Shields, not far off, had killed another deer, Lewis saw. And this was soon attacked in the same ravenous fashion. The gorge of the empty white men rose, but they looked on with pity too. Lewis ordered a fire built, and the finest steaks immediately roasted and shared by all.

Now the stock of the white men was up again. Cameahwait, with great ceremony, took off his superb tippet of silky otter dangling ermine tails and glittering with pearl, and laid it upon the white chief's shoulders. Lewis returned the compliment by placing his cocked hat and feather upon the grim, greased head of the chief. The Indians grunted with satisfaction at this exchange, and over their fed bellies.

Then they rode on again. Lewis had put in the hand of the foremost brave the flag of the United States; this would show any of Clark's party that the approaching Indians were allies. We must, Lewis thought, make a curious spectacle for these old hills to look down on! The amphitheatric sweep of Shoshone Cove, with its floor of sage and its tiers of watching ranges, lies like a stage for heroic event. And here came a strangely mingled troop, the savages dripping fringe and fur barbarically, the tattered white men adorned with Indian fineries, the gaunt red chief immensely dignified in the battered American army hat, and the glorious, candy-striped, starry banner rippling on before to announce to all the children of this land a destiny they could not yet spell out.

At dusk they came toward the forks where Lewis had left his note for Clark. Their hoofbeats approached hollowly in the great dim silence. There was no reek of camp smoke on the air, no glow of fire through the heavy

so far; they had reached the high place, the pass, the proving point of all their luck. Was it all to show to a man who had dared too boldly how little fate was really his to shape?

✍ XVII

AND HAD BILLY CLARK given up navigation? Did he fail of the mark by the last hard score of miles? When he was needed most, was he beyond reach?

You can imagine only one answer. That night when Cameahwait slept with Lewis's gun under his hand beside the defenseless white captain, William Clark, by swear-word and laughter, by pole and by towline and by the heart he could put into a heartless situation, had got the canoes to a spot within four miles of the Shoshones' encampment. Four miles away from the sleepless Lewis, Clark lay awake wishing his friend luck, asking God to keep an eye on him and the devil where he was.

The endurance of the men, he grimly admitted to himself, he had driven to its farthest. They had been asked to perform today the work of men of steel. But even steel has its tensile limits. He knew when they were reached. Luck would have to meet them in the morning.

Last night he had felt all tempers on edge. At the evening meal, Charbonneau had struck Sacajawea before everyone, and Clark's own temper at that rose to boiling.

But to prevent fighting right there in camp, he had to measure out his reproof in tones that must not quiver with the anger that he felt. An officer must treat every occurrence impersonally; he must have no favorites. But if there's any one of us to be prized now, he said to the wavering fire, it's Janey, bless her.

Sacajawea had stretched out in the superb repose of her young savagery, beyond the reach of any blow of Charbonneau's to hurt her now. For she lay at the threshold of home. This vast darkness, so wild and un-plumbed to the white men sleeping around her, that to them represented their farthest west as yet, the spring-board of their plunge into the absolute unknown, was her native rooftree. Upon home ground, darkness is not strange; it covers with kindliness familiar shapes and signs. And these crouching mountains were familiar as tame beasts to her; the very smell of the air, high, dry, pungent with the dust of sagebrush and the hint of pine, was the odor of her childhood. The frogs talked Sho-shone, and nothing that happened now could be any-thing but a good happening.

So she slept, the wonderful deep sleep of the returned exile.

They hadn't gone a mile after breakfast the next morning before Clark, who was walking a little behind the squaw and Charbonneau along the bank, heard a shout. It came from the Indian girl, and she was looking back at him, past Pomp between her shoulders, her face suddenly radiant. She stabbed the beyond with her

219

finger and began, to his astonishment, to dance. She clapped her hands, as she had seen the white men do, to tell him how happy she was. And there beyond her he perceived advancing a party of Indians—several men, a squaw, and a man in Indian dress whom he recognized as Drouillard.

The girl was now showing a degree of emotion he had never dreamed she could exhibit. She was like a little fountain of joy; she tried to express herself to Charbonneau, but she seemed almost unable, in this moment, to remember any Minnetaree. She pointed again at the approaching Indians, and then she put her fingers in her mouth and sucked them, looking earnestly at Clark, above this infantile gesture, with eyes that pleaded to be understood. And he did not fail to grasp her meaning; she had been suckled, she was telling him, in the same tribe as these people who were coming. Even Charbonneau cut a little caper of pleasure that his *femme* was right about something for once.

"Well, well, Janey, so we've found your folks, have we? Thank heaven for that! Hallo, Drouillard!" Clark shouted. "Where is Captain Lewis?"

"He very good. He wait for you near by with the big chief of these people." Drouillard loped forward and delivered his note.

But Clark, halfway through it, lifted his eyes to stare at Sacajawea, as a sob of feeling broke out of her throat. She was running into the arms of the approaching Shoshone squaw, and Clark's own throat felt suddenly a little thick. The two women clung together, parted to look at each other, and clung again in the Shoshone embrace, the right arm of each about the shoulders of the other, cheek pressed against cheek. He heard the quick whispering lilt of their exchange, and he realized that he had never heard Janey really talk before. To him, to Lewis, to Charbonneau, she had been always merely Indian, uneducated, speaking little, and showing less. So the white man assumes that a redskin is a slow-witted, thick-hided, inexpressive limb of creation. It never occurs to him to think how stupid, how foolish a white man may look to an Indian, or how poorly express himself. Clark thought, I take a lot back, Janey, little woman. I just didn't know; I didn't see.

Sacajawea, he noticed, had taken Pomp out of his basket and was holding him up to her friend. You do not need to know a language to understand what any two women are saying about a baby.

"Only seven months, you tell me?" exclaimed the ad-miring friend, as is only proper. "But how large for his age, how strong!" She took the baby's fist in eager fingers.

"And he is very intelligent, too," Sacajawea earnestly told her. "He has given no trouble at all to the white men, all the way that we have come from the Mandan lodges. Come, you shall meet my white captain," she declared, bursting with liberated pride.

All the way to the camp of Lewis and Cameahwait, the Indians sang with triumph. Their barbaric rhythms echoed across the wide vales between the sunny mountains. Soon, in the center of a little meadow, Clark, pressing ahead with Drouillard, saw Lewis with the red chief and his two headmen seated affably on smooth white antelope skins, like a king who awaits fellow royalty. Clark chuckled once more. So Meriwether had done it again!

The two captains clapped each other, eyes twinkling, solemnly around the shoulders in Shoshone fashion.

"Redhead!" said Lewis loudly. "My brother Redhead!" Under his breath he muttered, "Look out, Billy, they're not yet ready to trust us." And lifting his voice again, "Come and meet Cameahwait, the chief." He added in a murmur, "If we can only win him wholly, we are safe."

Cameahwait arose like a gentleman and striding up to Clark embraced him as heartily as a bear. Lewis concealed a smile as he watched Billy's face over Cameahwait's shoulder; the redheaded giant tottered, smothered in the Indian's embrace.

"Don't mind the national hug, Billy—it's just the hazing before you are initiated. You're being taken into the lodge," Lewis said.

"I make you my brother! I give you my name," cried Cameahwait, bestowing the most personal honor in an Indian's power. Then he tied six small shells in the hair of William Clark of Mulberry Hill, who accepted them with grave gratitude.

Scannon came bounding up at this point, to leap upon

Lewis in joy, and the Indians marveled to see the affection between man and beast, and to hear Lewis speak to him, and the dog perfectly understand his orders.

"Shake hands with the gentleman, Scannon," ordered Lewis, and the Newfoundland gave his huge paw to the astonished Shoshone chief. Then Lewis held his arm out straight from the shoulder and whistled, and the great beast trotted back a distance, measured with his eye, and came bounding over the hurdle. His master snapped his fingers, and Scannon stood on his hind legs, his forepaws paddling the air, and walked about like a man.

"Big medicine, eh, Chief?" said Clark affably to Cameahwait.

"And where," the chief asked in sign language, "is this man whose skin is wholly black? All the Shoshones want to look upon this black man."

"Drouillard," said Lewis, "go back and find York, and bring the squaw here too." But before the interpreter departed, he said through him elaborately to Cameahwait at the head of the gathered Shoshones, "Now you see that my brother Redhead has come, as we pledged you our guns that he would." And he waited.

But the Shoshones remained impassive; the guns stayed gripped in their hard fingers. Lewis kept on smiling, but a tingle ran up his spine. "Go on, Drouillard," he ordered and to Clark he murmured evenly, "I see we're not out of this yet."

Sacajawea came into the council circle with her eyes

downcast, as becomes a squaw. She had been brought here only as an interpreter. This was a moment of state and ceremony, not hers to show emotion or to possess a personality. She seated herself on the ground, her lids still lowered and her eyes directed at the spot before Lewis's feet, awaiting his orders.

"Tell them now," he commanded her with a faint urgency in his voice, "that we come as friends, that you know us to be good men. Make them believe you."

Charbonneau, standing stooped beside her, wove the words into Minnetaree. It was very hot in this open council circle; it was breathless, and the Indian smell was dominant on the air. Sacajawea, in the waiting stillness, began to speak in Shoshone. She kept her gaze still on the ground, but directed toward the feet of Cameahwait now; her voice was low and impersonal and grave.

"The white captains are very good men. They have protected me and brought me kindly back to my own country. So you can trust them. They have come a long way to seek for you, and they bring you presents. They wish to buy horses, and will pay good prices for them. They are men of honor. For the sake of our own honor you must treat them well. I, a Shoshone woman, have pledged it." And she raised her eyes to the chief's face.

For a moment the hot air tingled in silence. Then she leaped to her feet with a cry and ran to Cameahwait, a torrent of sudden tears sparkling upon her face.

"Elder brother!" she cried to him. "Elder brother!" And with a gesture of religious dignity and tenderness, she drew her blanket from her shoulders and swept it about those of the tall gaunt chief.

There was no Indian stolidity left in their little squaw, the captains saw. They saw her melt weeping into her brother's arms, and heard her voice come muffled from his breast. They smiled with tender comprehension, and yet they only half understood. They knew her gesture to have meant the two of them were of one family, one blood, but the closest of white families can never know what family means to an Indian. To a red woman there is no husband that cannot be replaced; she has no lover, only a master. But to be of the same blanket is a bond woven of threads pure and unbreakable. So the features of Cameahwait were suddenly and strangely worked into softness. He permitted himself no womanish tears, but the white men turned away at his voice, and looked at each other and spoke gently. Clark had a bevy of sisters, gay girls, some of the best of his comrades. Lewis had a little foster sister, for whose welfare, education and decorous upbringing he had a fatherly concern. Shannon was elder brother to three of this kind of female relation, who were accustomed to mutual teasing and tyranny. But this grim chief was fighting to conceal an emotion alien to all theirs, and more masterful. For him his sister was the only irreplaceable woman in the world. The blood of brotherhood was the blood of honor, of identity. There had come home to him a part of himself.

Suddenly Sacajawea raised her face and looked at her brother in shocked astonishment. She passed her hands over his hair that had been cut tragically short all over his head.

"You are in mourning! Who of our family is dead? Tell me now, quickly!"

He made his face stoic as stone. "Come now, younger sister. This is not the time to speak of these things. This is the council. The white chiefs are waiting."

Sacajawea drew herself visibly together, appearing tall for all her slight height. She turned to face the captains, the tears ignored upon her grave face.

"The chief is my brother," she said to them in Minnetaree. "Therefore he is your friend."

Then she resumed her place on the ground, with her eyes downcast, the sun glittering on her carven features where they still were wet.

So eloquently had the two Shoshones' embrace spoken for itself that the girl's short speech needed no translation. Charbonneau, however, stumbled it out in a voice of astonishment, and stood, in his usual hangdog way, looking at his wife with a mixture of pride and perplexity. *Parbleu*, he had not foreseen so powerful a brother-in-law when he bought the girl five years ago to be his slave!

Lewis arose, using white man's ceremony in his sudden uprush of exultation, and strode into the middle of the circle facing Cameahwait.

"We are gratified to see our friend Sacajawea reunited with her noble brother. We wish to tell him of our gratitude to his sister. She has guided the white men here, straight and true as an arrow, in order that they may know their brothers the Shoshones." He beckoned Shannon to come forward with the things with which he had provided him. "Our great Chief far in the East, whose name is Jefferson, sends greetings. He sends you this medal. It bears his face upon it, so that you may see that he is a good man. On the other side, you see, there is a picture of his hand clasping yours, and of a pipe of peace and a tomahawk to show that he wishes to trade with you."

Into the dark palm of Cameahwait he laid the little cast of Jefferson's serene countenance. Then from Shannon's arm he lifted a splendid blue American army coat with brass buttons and gold epaulettes, and draped it over Cameahwait's shoulders. The chief beamed with gracious pleasure, but when he was presented with a pair of scarlet leggings, he must again throw his arm around Lewis's shoulder and press his vermilion-painted cheek to the lean Virginian's.

"He says," Sacajawea reported through Charbonneau, "that the friends of his sister are his brothers. He restores your guns. He offers you many horses, and guides to take you over the mountains. They will bring you to a river where you can find timber to build canoes. That river will lead you to the great lake of water in the west."

After their captain, the three men who had surrendered their guns and their lives into the hands of the Shoshones the night before stepped forward and received their weapons back again with ceremony.

And at this triumphant moment, the two Fields boys, who had been sent out hunting, came in with four deer —a feast for all, and Indians and white men broke up in milling enthusiasm.

Between Clark and Lewis there was no need of speech, of mutual congratulation. Only they exchanged a long look, two men who had been sure each of the other, and who both recognized devoutly that they had received help beyond the power of either.

Sacajawea, who had learned now from her brother that her mother and father and sister had all died since she was stolen from home, went apart from the feasting. She sat cross-legged upon the earth under a little alder, her hands empty upon her knees, and bowed her head. So long she sat there, with the river going softly by and the alder leaves rustling, that a yellow warbler and his mate came flitting back to the little tree and foraged there in quiet confidence.

❧ XVIII

THE NEXT DAY, Sunday the eighteenth of August, was the thirty-second birthday of Meriwether Lewis. And on it he set down some reflections in his journal. It must be remembered that there are two Lewises in print. There is his actual narrative written day by day of the expedition; this is the source book of all that we know of the most unknown illustrious character in American history. And, by contrast, there is the joint narrative of the two captains, which is an edited work bearing the stamp of other natures besides Meriwether's. In this, the so-called standard journal of the expedition, the two commanders, and indeed all the men, are blended more or less into a composite personality and tale. If accepted as such a composite, it is not at all misleading; it is in itself a wonderfully rich, ever fascinating picture of those united labors and separate souls.

The individual journals that have survived to us, of Meriwether Lewis, William Clark, Patrick Gass, John Ordway, Joseph Whitehouse, and Charles Floyd who died before the Mandan villages were reached, are the materials out of which the formal, final report was worked. And they tell what manner of man each writer was. They are liberally seasoned with human, fallible personality; there are plentiful mistakes—mistakes of estimated distances and heights, of the identities of members of the fauna and flora, of the Indian names for persons and places and things. In these separate journals we learn that the commanders swore, that certain men, plainly named, were wenchers and others forever leaving things behind or getting lost, that the lot of them got boils and diarrhea and cramps in the stomach. The simpler diarists wrote as ungrammatically as they talked; they were keen observers, who often put in more curious small details than their captains, but they wasted very little time on recording their sentiments. Their most vivid comments are upon food, fright, cold, heat, sore feet, strained backs, mosquitoes and fleas. William Clark wrote with an irrepressible gusto, in the style of a gentleman; almost alone among the diarists he puts in the humor, usually at the expense of the Indians, York or Charbonneau, and he is open and tender about the girl he calls Janey. Of all the manuscripts now reposing in the vaults of the Library of Congress, it is probable that none is so whimsical and wild in its spelling of the English language as Billy Clark's.

The journal of Meriwether Lewis is a document that we cannot read without reverence and melancholy. Usually the diary of a highly civilized and educated man with an introspective nature is a literary work composed at a desk, by one for whom self-expression is either his job in life or an incorrigible habit. Meriwether Lewis was not a poet, not a philosopher, not a gossip, not a historian, not a Job full of complaints to the management, nor a savoring Amiel. He was a soldier, a private secretary, and in him reserve was a first impulse. What he wrote was written on the march, on his knee probably, with all the day's fatigues to slow the pen. And yet, however exhausted, elated, disappointed, anxious or angered we perceive that he must have been, every word that he puts down appears to have been weighed and chosen with judgment. So that his writing has a polish that never left him even in howling wilderness. And since he was a man who acutely realized every moment that he lived, there shines between the lines the light of his spirit, guarded but purely flaming.

On this birthday spent at the foot of the Lemhi pass, he confided to his diary some reflections upon his life thus far. Since, he wrote, he had "in all human probability now existed about half the period which I am to remain in this sublunary world," it was time, he deemed, to find out what he had accomplished "to further the happiness of the human race, or to advance the information of the succeeding generation."

For half his life at least he had dreamed and planned this moment when the gates of the Rockies would swing wide to him and he would see his way clear down the waters of the Columbia to the sea. For more than two years of grueling physical effort and heaviest responsibility he had been constantly working toward this point.

To us his dedication looks utterly disinterested; it is a soldier's, an explorer's, a patriot's. And here now he rests a moment, gathering forces for further trials and dangers, and looking critically at what he has already achieved. "I viewed with regret," he concluded, "the many hours I have spent in indolence, and now soarly felt the want of that information had they been judi, ciously expended. But since they are past and cannot be recalled, I dash from me the gloomy thought, and re, solve in future to redouble my exertions and at least indeavour to promote those two primary objects of human existence" (happiness of the human race and information of the succeeding generations) "by giving them the aid of that portion of talents which nature and fortune have bestowed upon me; or in future, to live *for mankind* as I have heretofore lived *for myself.*"

Here we have him, the eternal, unresting pathfinder, never able to enjoy the leagues he has put behind him, but forever straining forward toward the next accomplishment. Men like that are the men who have got us as far as we are in civilization; only they can get us the rest of the way.

And beside a man like that, you may always look for a woman. She need not be able to see ahead as his eagle's eyes can see. It suffices if she sees in him the force to be forwarded, guided, upheld.

Uniquely the woman beside Meriwether Lewis was one to whom he felt the most impersonal gratitude. She was not even of his color. They could not so much as

talk together in one tongue. But they lived for one purpose, since her purpose was only his.

Look at them well. They are a man and a woman
bound by no tie of flesh, of sentiment, of loyalty even
so loftily in common as the same flag. Sacajawea could
not really understand what that fluttering banner stood
for. Yet when you look at it today, remember that she
put five of the stars in it. She did this, if you like, for
the love of a man, a white man. But it was a love as pure
and clear and cold as the sources of Missouri and Columbia. And out of it has descended to us as mighty a flow.

Every day for the next fortnight Sacajawea was busy,
in the most intellectual employ she had ever had in her
life, translating for Lewis and the Indians. At the camp
where she had first met her brother, in the Lemhi pass,
or down the other side in the valley of the Lemhi where
she had been born, she was needed at all hours of the
day and many of the night. She had picked up a lot of
French by this time, since Charbonneau talked it with
the captains and the watermen and explained it to her
in Minnetaree, and learned some small English as well.
Besides which, Lewis and Shannon now knew some Shoshone and a bit of the sign language got from Drouillard.
So this medley of tongues and gestures flew about the
camps in a current that made meaning. For the Shoshones were a sociable people, even chatty and fond of
jokes.

Lewis was chafing with impatience to be off and over
the mountains. Though the days were hot, there was

frost every night now, and the snows on the peaks re-
minded him that he would have to get through the
Rockies before winter fell upon him and loaded them
all with its chains. Cameahwait, however, was in no
hurry to part with his guests. Every day Sacajawea had
to explain to the captains that her brother had invited
yet another and more distant group of influential headmen to come for a parley. To the Indian mind, this sort
of agreeable ceremoniousness was what time was made
for and, whatever they lacked, the Lemhis had never
known want of time. Therefore not only headmen but
whole villages and their babes and dogs came trooping.
They all expected speeches and presents, and Lewis
dared offend not one of them. Cordial relations must be
firmly built with these people, not only in behalf of the
expedition but for the nation that was to follow it here.
Therefore Lewis endlessly, ceremoniously gave and accepted, and suffered oratory. For he saw that this was
the climax of the history of the Lemhi band.

At the center of that climax stood Sacajawea. Probably never in tribal story had a squaw been such a heroine to her own people. She had brought them all glory,
a glory full of the mystery and potency of medicine,
and made them all feel how important they were to the
white man who now for the first time came among them.
She, a Shoshone, had done this. They saw that the white
chiefs depended upon her and deferred to her. They
realized that after her would come wealth in trade, alliance with power, and in that moment, perhaps, was born

the friendship that the Shoshones were to maintain with the Americans. When fifty years later every warrior of the tribe rode into General Crook's camp as an ally, after Custer's disaster on the Little Bighorn, they came on fire with a loyalty kindled by Sacajawea now. The child of her dead sister, a little boy that Sacajawea adopted now as her own son, was to be one of the chiefs who saved Crook from the trap of the Sioux; Shoogan—Basil, the white men called him—with his Shoshones held the rear so that the Americans could re-form their line.

Now this sturdy red child looked up at the strange woman, great and beautiful, who had come out of the East with the white men to bring him honor and safety, and to place on his tongue a new good food called sugar, a taste like rapture in the mouth.

Thus to her own people was restored Sacajawea, Canoe Launcher. Stolen away from them five years ago, the most altering years in a human life, she had now in her hands more than she had ever longed for in her slavery and exile. She was the great woman of her tribe, at the seat of their power, her brother the chief beside her, and children to raise to honor about her.

Here, then, she might have stayed. For who thinks that Charbonneau had no price for her? Or that Cameahwait would not have met it? Here the work which she had been brought to do was finished. From here on there could be nothing but more fatigue and hardship, more risk to the baby, and a resumption of the humble place a red woman must take among white soldiers. And, at the end, which promised glory and reward to them, nothing was promised her except Charbonneau's packs again for her back, and his insolence and jealousy.

But not only was the blood of the white men in her child Pomp, but in her own blood ran now an inalterable devotion to them. Here at the Lemhi pass, where Sacajawea had her choice to make, was consummated some marriage of the American soul with the soul of aboriginal America.

Yet Sacajawea was no abstraction; she was a high-hearted, young, adventure-loving little savage. Let them go on without her and discover the Big Water, while she squatted here safe in the camp of relatives? Not this girl. Whatever tears she may have shed at parting from her people were dried by the wind that struck her face as the expedition set forth again into the mountains.

And what, if you care to remember it, had the conqueror of all Europe been attaining in these last weeks so triumphant for Lewis and Clark and the American nation? The August sun that saw them consolidating their peaceful alliance with the indispensable Lemhi band, looked down upon a stocky, sweating figure pacing the sands of Boulogne in a ferment of curdling ambition. A hundred and thirty-two thousand obedient troops waited behind him; everything was calculated for their transport across the Channel in two tides. Now was the moment to invade England!

But the moments, hot and fretful, buzzed past his irritated nose. He slapped an imperious hand into his other empty palm. Where in the name of God was Villeneuve with the French fleet? Could not even an emperor count upon his lieutenants?

Not always. Villeneuve, catching a glimpse of Nelson from the corner of his nervous eye, lost faith, lost heart, lost touch; he sailed for Cadiz, not for England, and the vaunted Armada that was to sweep into the Channel upon the tight island never even formed.

Josephine quailed when her husband came striding back to Paris, his hat jammed over his bloodshot eyes and in his mouth imprecations upon his vacillating admiral. Again the imperial fist struck into the grasping palm. If England by invasion was a lost hope, he would have Austria, and all of Russia too! The brilliant military orders began to flow from the short strutting figure, orders for those next illustrious victories that led toward his destruction.

Lewis and Clark were toiling over the Bitterroots. For the previous half year they had had a yellow-eyed demon of river for their road, and tricky cockleshells for their transport. Now they had a troop of pack-sore, half-savage horses to bear them, and soon no trail at all, instead the unpenetrated, gloomy forest, never yet blazed, that rose up over the serrated ridges and sank into the canyons. Spruces tall as ship masts, bull pine and lodgepole pine and quaking aspen closed their ranks against the explorers and drove the toiling defile sometimes even into the torrential rocky beds of the wild cold rivers. Then they must hack and tear a slow passage

237

up the mountainsides again and over the crests. And here the tomahawk of premature winter swept upon them, lifting scalplocks and knifing marrow. Sleet burned their faces, snow blinded them, and the wind cut their vitals as the thongs of the packs cut into the whinnying horses who slipped and fell down the steep ravines and had to be hauled back, crippled.

Now they came among strange people, the Ootlashoots and the Tushapaws, whose women let their hair fall wildly over their faces and who talked in the guttural clucking of unknown fowl. Now the game hid from them in the forest, and their stock of flour was at last exhausted. Now the men, who had endured so many pangs, felt the first bite of famished craving in their bellies. These wind-blasted ridges withheld from them even water; they were too high to find springs frequently, and they must melt the snow to drink, as sometimes they must feed on the meat of one of their pack animals. The horses, some of them, failed, and had to be left; none of the men failed, ever. Snow buried the faint Indian track from them, and soaked through their thin moccasins till they stamped to know if their numb feet were still under them. The silence of the forest closed about them unattacked; no shots broke it, for there was little to shoot at. The men were nearly naked by this time; the skin was taut over features set in that American grin of grit. No man, not even the Virginia gentlemen captains, was so fastidious that he could not down the flesh of horse or Indian dog gratefully. But Sacajawea, a

Shoshone with Shoshone pride in this matter, went stoically hungry rather than touch such detested meat.

Down the western slope of the Bitterroots they came, in a long, swaying, creaking defile, cutting a slow way along the declivity through tamarack and hackmatack, fir and spruce and pine, with the roar of westward-running waters far below them in the canyon, and the threat of ice and snow hanging above. In these forests fed with rain winds from the Pacific, the great roots spread and twined and locked, and treacherous moss overlay them. It was cold among the trees as it was dark. As the campfires struggled against the chill and gloom, the men laughed and shook their heads to remember how they had sweltered such a little while ago under the cottonwoods of the Missouri. Making out with watery berries and tough horseflesh, they recalled to one another ruefully the steaks they had broiled, of buffalo and venison, back on the plains.

Hot or cold, dry or wet, they took one thing with another. Now the captains foresaw that soon pack-travel must come to an end. Just as on the dwindling Jefferson they had been obliged to abandon their boats at last, so now they must quit the failing horses, find navigable water, and timber to build boats again. Neither spruce nor pine nor fir would do; these check and split and would not last in the rivers.

Lewis's fingers, plucking at a branch as he rode, found that they were questioning a new foliage, a little flat ferny spray of overlapping needles. He looked up quickly; there ahead a grove of ruddy columns was closing in about the cavalcade. The giant shaggy trunks soared into darkness, but he knew them, *arbor-vitae*, tree of life.

Here is a grain to turn the axe blade; this is the tree of which the Nootka Indians carve their tall totems, and the Chinooks make their eternal warships, charring the big boles hollow with fire. This is canoe cedar, and Sacajawea, by tribal lore, knew it when she saw it. She was riding behind Lewis, and when he turned in his saddle, she was smiling; pointing to the monstrous and seaworthy trees, she made for him in a sweeping gesture the shape of a long canoe.

The next day, Napoleon's armies crossed the Rhine.

The end of September, so mournful in northwestern Europe, and the opening of October that has an American tingle to it in our own Northwest, kept the men under Clark and Lewis busy felling the stubborn fifty-foot cedars and burning them out into boats. Saddles and some of the powder were buried in a cache, the horses branded and delivered into the care of Indians, and on October seventh the canoes were launched and once more the men felt river power buoy them recklessly along. Days later, they came flashing down the Snake, over the shoals and rapids, past the sage and driven dust of the badlands, to the spot where its troubled waters pour into the beryl-colored depth of the Columbia.

On October nineteenth the Austrians, overwhelmed, surrendered at Ulm. The next day Clark saw, from the cliffs of the Columbia, a sudden white head rising, a dead volcano in a shroud of snow. He knew it for Mount St. Helens, the very peak laid down by the navigator Vancouver as visible from the mouth of the Columbia. When the men were told, they nodded to one another, grinning in laconic satisfaction.

The throats of Napoleon's legionaries still were hoarse from cheering the dazzling maneuver at Ulm, when, at Trafalgar, Nelson died in the arms of victory and Bonaparte's fleet was strewn upon the bottom of the Atlantic.

On the second day of November, the broadening bosom of Columbia carried the expedition's tiny fleet of dugouts twenty-nine miles, until at last it lifted in a great sigh visible to the exultant eyes of the Americans. Tidewater reached! They slept that night in the deep calm of conifer forests, full fed and tranquil.

Napoleon was then camped at Ried; a sharp frost pinched the sentries. The officers stepped briskly in and out of headquarters where the Emperor sat heavy-browed with concentration and resolve. For, since Trafalgar had blotted France out as a naval power, he had sworn to ruin England through conquests on the continent. Tomorrow he would be in full march against sixty thousand Austrians, a hundred thousand Russians.

The Columbia broadened, a mile and more of majestic water, studded with green islands. Upon the forested shores dwelt Indians, Skilloots and Chilluckittequaws and the Wahkiahcums who had flattened heads and dressed in furs and cedar-bark. These people became friends as soon as they saw Sacajawea, for they knew that no war party of whites would be graced by a red woman and her child. The morning of November seventh was rainy, with fog so thick the explorers could not see across the river. But the wet white air smelled of salt. And with high hearts, with filling sails and flashing paddles, they drove into the blanketed unknown. As the day climbed toward meridian, the fog began to gleam, to glisten, to shift and lift and melt away to blue, and there before them clear water widened to an unlimited horizon, and they could hear the Pacific roaring and tumbling upon rocks that were America's western boundary, now established by these thirty-one men and a woman.

At Malmaison, Josephine fretted idly over her trinkets, feeling, in the latest letter of her husband's from the front, the chill of her waning day. Napoleon wasted few words on love; he was making ready for the kill. In the sad Austrian skies the crows were gathering for Austerlitz.

It was Sacajawea who chose for her captains the site of their winter camp, a few miles from the sea on the south side of the mouth of the Columbia. The winds and the rains had set in violently and would here endure till spring. Wet rags of deerskin hung on men thinned to bone and muscle; with a will they went to raising the walls of a home. Upon a little height that overlooked tidewater, they felled, first of the giants around them, an enormous fir, leaving its stump to serve as a big table.

About this they raised the walls of the fort. The Indians, the Clatsop tribes, came in groups to watch and admire. The rain fell endlessly; the men, their stomachs sticking to their spines with famine, hewed and hammered. The beautiful balsam-fir, they found, split into two-foot boards obediently. The hunters ranged for the scanty elk. The huts began to rise, day upon day. In the meat-house game was hung. It rained, it hailed, it blew. Snow showed for the first time on distant Saddle mountain. The cold breath of the ocean came haunting through the woods, and the gulls flew before the wind, white against the black trees. So high the storms drove the water, even here in this backwash of the Columbia, that the captains feared their canoes would be shattered, and they sank them for safety in the creek, with stones in their charred bellies. The Clatsops came everlastingly trading, stealing, pandering; when Sacajawea went digging wappatoo root her dress hung loose now, for she had given her blue belt, that Lewis might have the sea otter skins he wanted from the Clatsop chief. By Christmas Fort Clatsop stood solid to the weather within its stockade.

Napoleon had been building too. He had been ingeniously constructing a new order for Europe, erected out of elaborate alliances and espousals and puppet coronations. On his brother Joseph he placed the crown of Naples. His favorite brother Louis, now married to Josephine's daughter Hortense, he made King of the Netherlands. He bustled Talleyrand off to become his feudal vassal in the newly created Italian state of Beneventum; his general Bernadotte he set up as liege lord of something called Pontecorvo. He married sixth cousins of the Beauharnais family off to Rhine princes, and the Princess of Württemberg must wed his brother Jerome as soon as he could get the young fool free of the Patterson woman of Baltimore.

That house of cards, of pasteboard kings and queens, raised on the rotting corpses of Austerlitz and held together only by sexual unions with no heart in them, was all to topple and collapse. But out of Fort Clatsop, where those thirty-two waited and hungered and kept up heart till the spring of 1806, have grown the strong young cities whose history is their future, and the broad green farms between the white-browed mountains, where the winy apples glow in the orchards and the timothy of the morning is a drop of cream upon the udder when the evening milking is begun.

❧ XIX

NOW, in the capital city, it was harder to hope. Another summer's wheat was threshed; its corn was in the bin; another year of the young nation's life was garnered. There was little left of the old Federalist opposition, in the fine October of 1806. But every month now—and the months had been so many!—thinned the confidence of Thomas Jefferson in the safe return of Lewis and his men.

The last letter he had received from his former secretary had been dated the seventh of April, 1805, at Fort Mandan. A year and a half ago, that was. Jefferson gently lifted the mockingbird from his forefinger back into its cage, and shook his head.

A year and a half was a long time, even in those days. For a party exploring into the unknown, with all the difficulties and dangers that it may conceal, such absence is like the sound of a tolling bell that you hope is only the ringing in your own ears.

If Thomas Jefferson had been another sort of man he would have begun to reproach himself for the rashness of the enterprise on which he had sent his young friend.

But Jefferson was one of the most serene men who ever got into a fight or shouldered trouble. He was a man who believed that nothing is so practical as an ideal. So, if there was no fundamental flaw in the plans, there was little likelihood of failure, no matter how long delayed the outcome. He cocked his head a trifle at the preening mocker in its cage; in a couplet of Pope's he found argument.

" 'And if the means be just, the conduct true—' " he murmured. Turning away, he heard a sound of hoof beats coming faintly through closed windows from the sickle of drive before the White House door.

The letter which was then at once put into his hands had been drafted a month before, as follows:

St. Louis, September 23rd, 1806.

Sir: It is with pleasure that I announce to you the safe arrival of myself and party at this place with our papers and baggage. no accedent has deprived us of a single member of our party since I last wrote you from the Mandans in April 1805. In obedience to your orders we have penetrated the Continent of North America to the Pacific Ocean and suficiantly explored the interior of the country to affirm that we have discovered the most practicable communication which dose exist across the continent by means of the navigable branches of the Missouri and Columbia Rivers—

Jefferson read on, his pulses pounding like a young man's again, his eyes rushing through Lewis's details of routes and passes, rivers and fur animals and Indian tribes:

—We left fort Clatsop where we wintered on the pacific Ocean the 27th of March last and arrived at the foot of the Rocky Mts. on the 10th of May here we were detained untill the 24th of June in consequence of the snow rendering those mountains impassable, had it not been for this detention I should have joined you at Montechello in this month agreeably to the promise made you previous to our departure from the Mandans—

The President whipped off his glasses and buried his face a moment in his hands with something between a hearty laugh and a sob. His former secretary's young correctness under even the wildest circumstances went to his heart. Meriwether had grace and could be supple with it, yet he never really unbent. But oh! thought Jefferson, the fidelity of the boy! He always came out right, just like a beautiful solution in Euclid. Jefferson blew his nose, and settled his spectacles to read the rest. The letter ended thus:

—The anxiety which I feel to return once more to the bosom of my friends is a sufficient guarantee that no time will be expended unnecessarily in this quarter. the rout by which I purpose travelling is from hence by Cahokia Vincennes LouisVill Kᵗʸ. the Craborchard Abington Fincastle, Stanton and Charlotsville to Washington. any letters directed to me at Louisvill 10 days

247

after the receipt of this will most probably meet me at that place. I am very anxious to learn the state of my friends in Albemarle particularly whether my mother is yet living. I am with every sentiment of esteem your most Ob^t. Servt.

Meriwether Lewis.

Capt. 1st U' S Reg^t Infty.

The President of the United States.

The President of the United States let out a great breath, and strode across the room to the map on the wall, his hands going out to it before he could reach it. So now the continent, like a flag, was fully unfurled! The cramped folds upon this little old map were obsolete. Soon, he exulted, he would have another to put up here, drafted from the observations of the expedition. Soon, into that vast territory not yet charted even upon the White House wall, would go trooping a people, a nation. They would be, they would have to be, some of the best and bravest of the country's men and women, he saw. For he was the leader who never doubted his followers; he was the man, of all our greatest men, whose eyes saw farthest west.

And West has been our national direction from the beginning. We early claimed to own it, flintlock, walnut stock, and lean barrel. We rose up now, once the way had been shown, and pressed against the winds, the westerlies and chinooks, till we came to autumn plenty, out where the pumpkin sun drops ripe.

Four months after the expedition reached St. Louis, the one cannon in the town of Fincastle, an old Revolutionary piece, recoiled with a shudder from its every enthusiastic bellow. The breath of the citizens' chairman, Mr. Patrick Lockhart, was frosty on the air as he thundered his own kindly bombast of welcome to the illustrious explorers Mr. Clark and Mr. Lewis. Clark, his red head bared to the gray sky, the corners of his mouth burying secret amusement, stepped forward to make a short speech in a style to suit the occasion. Lewis did not speak that day; this was Clark's day, and these were Clark's friends, and it was matter for his own secret amusement that out of a dozen alternative routes to Washington Billy had insisted on this one.

That night the candles and the hearthfires of the Hancock mansion set the windows to blazing on all sides.

"Well, now, and which is she?" twinkled Lewis to Clark, rubbing from his hands the frost they had left outside, as the black domestic took the officers' cloaks and hats.

Billy Clark's eyes darted through the garden of womenfolk in the big polished room beyond them, missing all the men, and skipping the ladies. "There isn't a child in the room," he said, with bewildered disappointment.

Mary, Caroline, John and young George Hancock— there they all were, moving among their guests. And here was Mrs. Hancock sweeping upon him with cordial delight, to carry both heroes off to be presented to those worthy of the honor.

Such are so seldom the young and beautiful! Clark bowed over a ringed and withered hand, straightened, and suddenly gasped. Across the room she was smiling to him over her shoulder, her mouth cool, her eyes merry, a woman in white satin with the face of a child he had loved.

Abruptly he drew his friend away from the distinguished ancient; Meriwether winced under the fingers gripping his arm.

"Miss Judith, may I have the honor to present to you my friend and companion, Captain Meriwether Lewis?"

The girl gave her eyes and her slim hand to Meriwether, curtseying. "An overwhelming honor for me, Captain Lewis," she daintily acknowledged. Her fan went into play. "But Captain Clark mistakes me, sir. My name is Julia, Julia Hancock."

"You used to be Judy," Billy bluntly accused.

"To my intimates I am still," she acknowledged, defending herself demurely with the breath of the stiff lace in her hand.

"Then posterity will forever miscall a certain river near the Great Falls of the Missouri by the name Judith's River," Lewis solemnly said.

"Is it a pretty stream?" queried Julia, toying with the ivory sticks.

"The most beautiful river in Louisiana," Clark assured her. "You must go meet Judy's sisters, Meriwether," he commanded in a mockery of the authority he had used to the men on the trip.

They were cordial to the great Captain Lewis, those sisters. Yet he was melancholy that night. His was the sad gift of foretaste, if not prevision. Lewis's name is never again linked with the girl for whom *he* named a river. But within a year Julia Hancock was married to William Clark, and within another she had borne him a son whom they named Meriwether Lewis.

When the captains at last arrived in Washington, Clark was made Superintendent of Indian Affairs, and Lewis nothing less than Governor of all Louisiana. Here at last was work for his capabilities, work to last him a lifetime. Here was the official reward of all his labors. From the acts of Lewis while Governor, we see the power of that essential justice in him, when used by an administrator of authority.

But from the times of George Washington on, there has been a race of rodents, having small but numerous places in government employ, who make it their function to disallow the expenditures of those who travel in the field for their country, and to dishonor, if possible, drafts necessarily made upon national credit to meet far off, unseen contingencies. So somebody contrived to create disorder in Lewis's conscientious accounts. Therefore in the autumn of 1809 Governor Lewis was obliged to set forth from St. Louis toward the capital, with his papers, much of his original journals, and a large sum of public monies, to confront this nameless stupid.

Grinder's Stand, on the Natchez Trace in Tennessee, was a lonely house serving the infrequent wayfarer, the last white man's on entering Indian territory. Old man Grinder, some of his neighbors said, had Indian blood in him. None of them knew much about him; he didn't welcome the curious; his woman kept a slatternly house, with a girl, Polly, to wait on what guests ever came. This much we know about Grinder and his inn toward which Lewis came riding at sundown on October eleventh, and we know too that there rode behind him as servants a negro boy and a Spanish halfbreed. Sometimes they let him get well out of sight, lagging where they could have talked in low voices together; each one of them was armed. Their hoofbeats came always thudding behind him, until the dim lights of Grinder's Stand were reached.

No one less than President Jefferson bears witness for us that to Meriwether Lewis came periods of profound melancholy. All of us know the depression that can fall upon us when important business is frustrated by some bungling fool. How ugly life can look when we are not believed in, and when some sordid charge against us of peculation is hinted at!

But to this wretched tavern on a fair evening in the fall of 1809 there came riding a man for whom no trial had ever proved too much. When he has crossed its threshold he is lost to our sure sight in a dark web of many stories. Yet it is not conceivable to anybody who has followed him to the Pacific and back, that it was he who fired the two shots that shocked Polly awake two hours before the dawn.

The Grinder woman, it seems, would not let her run outside and around to the stranger's door. Grinder had early disappeared, after a little talk with his guest, and did not show himself again that night. The negro boy and the halfbreed were clean gone by morning, and it was not till day that Polly was allowed to go into the room where the gentleman had gone to bed in his bear and buffalo robes upon the dirty floor. One bullet, the girl saw, had been sent into his heart, and one into his brain.

Then Grinder's woman went through the dead man's effects. There were just two bits in his pocket; his dispatch case had been broken open and emptied of all money and papers; his watch was gone too.

Months later, it appeared in New Orleans, in a pawnshop. Grinder, too, turned up in time; they tried him and had to let him go. The servants were never discovered again.

That other lonely figure, Alexander Wilson, lover too of wilderness, who found his friends more among birds than men, came by this way just a year after the fatal night. He stopped and talked long with the innkeeper's wife, in whose likely tale cannot be found the Lewis of the journals. Wilson stood a long while by the grave where Lewis lies hidden forever; the place was not far off the common path, the ornithologist writes, with a few loose rails thrown over it.

I gave Grinder money to put a post fence round it, to

shelter it from the hogs and from the wolves, and he
gave me his written promise that he would do it. I left
this place in a very melancholy mood, which was not
much allayed by the prospect of the gloomy and savage
wilderness which I was just entering alone.

A monument stands there now. On it are Jefferson's
own words in praise of the friend who was like a son to
him: "His courage was undaunted; his firmness and perseverance yielded to nothing but impossibilities; a rigid
disciplinarian, yet tender as a father of those committed
to his charge; honest, disinterested, liberal, with a sound
understanding and a scrupulous fidelity to truth."

Upon that side of the broken column of marble which
faces the coldest winds is written an epitaph arranged
from the Latin:

> *Immaturus obi: sed tu felicior annos*
> *Vive meos, Bona Respublica! Vive tuos.*

So Meriwether Lewis speaks forever to this nation:
Young I died. But thou, O great Republic, live out in
happiness those years I would have had. Live out thine
own!

☙ XX

THROUGH THE TREE of life the gale of mortality is always threshing. So that the leaves are falling in all seasons, pushing forth too, spreading green, turning sere, some early blasted, some wrenched away, and some silvered to the veins and at last cut adrift by the tree itself and given to the air and earth.

Thirty-one men, one woman and a baby, all of them mortals. Potts was the first to go, just one of the men but a good one. Trapping up around the Jefferson, he was suddenly surrounded by Blackfeet, and because he knew the ways in which they chose to put to death a man when they caught him, he shoved out in his canoe into the river, a clear target for their arrows, and so died clean, riddled like a pincushion.

So some of the thirty-one went back to the wilderness? you say. Yes, there were some went back, some you couldn't keep home. Why, Colter turned back at the Mandan villages, when the expedition reached there; his captains set it down in their journals in wonderment, that a man could be so close to safety, family, comfort, and yet start back to face the very perils and hardships from which he had earned a long rest.

He disappeared for a long time into wilderness no man knew. And when he got back, he couldn't get anybody to believe what he'd seen. He'd followed the Yellowstone up to its source and, by God, that was the place where Hell came up through the crust. Talk about brimstone and sulphur and bubbling lakes of Gehenna! He did talk, and they laughed at him.

So he told about the time the Blackfeet got him, stripped him naked, and made him run the gantlet right across miles of prickly-pear. Those devils came after him, mile after mile, yelling and shooting and him dodging the arrows. Hid under a raft in the river, he did, while they powwowed over his head. He could draw a long bow, John Colter could, his delighted listeners chuckled. Those fountains of boiling water, bedad! Who could believe in any of it?

But all the same, because he twice turned back from the edge of civilization, the great exploring party sent out by John Jacob Astor stopped by on their way overland to see if they couldn't get Colter to come along for guide.

He chuckled under the covers, to think how he'd turned them down, and all their money. When he went, he went for his own good reasons. When he didn't go, he had a reason too. He hugged it now, working an arm under her shoulders till his hand came round and found the young curve of her cheek.

Gibson died in the same year as Lewis. Next year it was Drouillard, the mighty hunter of the expedition who had kept them all alive at Fort Clatsop, bringing down elk where others saw no elk. Drouillard the halfbreed, the swift runner, who could talk to all the alien tribes with his quick fingers. It was at the Three Forks of the Missouri that Blackfoot arrows found him. He fought, using his standing horse for a bulwark; then the horse buckled and rolled over, and Drouillard lay behind the dead bulk, still shooting, to the end.

Mr. Nicholas Biddle of Philadelphia, banker, scholar, patron of literature, ruthless maker and unmaker of senators and lesser fry, was finding in 1810 that he couldn't go on with editing the journals of the expedition without some help, because of the lamentable gaps in Lewis's pages. Presumably the missing parts were seized from the captain's dispatch box on the night of his murder, but not being money or letters of credit, they had been considered worthless and strewn no one could say where. So, Clark wrote, he was sending Mr. Biddle the man whom, of all the expedition, he considered the most acute and best educated.

Twenty-three years old, George Shannon stumped into Mr. Biddle's spacious study on his peg-leg. The Arikaras had done that to him. In a party under Sergeant Pryor, George had turned back at St. Louis to escort home a Mandan chief ally, and on the Dakota plains they were attacked. There had been small help there for his wound, so that he'd had to lie eighteen months in the army hospital at Fort Bellefontaine, where they took the leg off. And when at last he got home, after all that, Jane Milligan sent her runaway son back to school!

"Mr. Shannon," cried Nicholas Biddle, at the end of their first day's work together, "you are a treasure trove. You light up these pages till I feel I might have been there myself!" And the banker puffed happily with borrowed heroics.

George Shannon, looking at him from under long black lashes, smiled a kind young smile. He thought of McNeal treed by a grizzly for three hours, of Drouillard saving his skull, when the canoe swept back upon him, by diving to the bottom, of Windsor, half over a ninety-foot precipice above the Missouri, inching back to safety, and of Reuben Fields stabbing a Blackfoot from spine to breastbone in one blow, when Captain Lewis was surprised in the night.

Politely George answered, "Had you indeed been with us, sir, you could not have played a part so valuable as the part you take now."

Amiably dismissed by the great man, George stumped away to his privacy. He wanted to write this evening to a Miss Price, Ruth Snowden Price, a rose he had found just opening in Lexington, Kentucky, while he was attending Transylvania University there. But when his letter was finished, and he had put out the light, he lay a long time awake between the smooth sheets, and it was not of Ruth that he found himself thinking. Wonder was filling him that he could ever have been the boy, hard, wet, hungry, laughing, who had known the exultation of desire for a woman he meant never to take, a red woman, a savage, a girl with glossy braids and night-sky eyes. She was a world away from him now, wherever she was, the world of a scholar and a gentleman.

All the time the wind of mortality is rushing through the tree. It comes to the Mandan villages as smallpox; the bodies turned black before they could be buried. Afraid to touch them, the living dragged the corpses by hooks under the chin and burned them. And still the white man's putrid fever destroyed them by the hundreds, till the race was smitten to its knees, to its face. Word came to the Mandans' white friends that Toussaint Charbonneau had lost an Indian wife in the epidemic.

So people believed that Sacajawea had died. You can find it in histories of the time, in some encyclopedias still. Thus miserably, some have thought, she perished.

But it was Otterwoman who died. For Sacajawea was living in St. Louis then, in Redhead's Town, as the Indians called it, since Clark had been made Governor of Louisiana Territory in Lewis's stead. He lived there always, holding a kindly court to red and white alike. He was always ready to show his trophies to every guest, his sumptuous gifts from chiefs all up the Missouri and down the Columbia, Tillamooks and Clatsops, Nez-Percés and Flatheads, Shoshones and Mandans. And every month he settled the bill for Pomp's schooling: four dollars for a hat, a dollar and fifty cents for a lesson book, fifty dollars for board—so the items still stand.

He had hoped for better than this. But at the Mandan villages he had had to say goodbye to Pomp—"my little dancing boy," as his own writing has it. It was at Fort Clatsop that Clark had finally lost his heart to this mite of humanity. When Pomp was desperately sick, weaned from the safety of mother's milk to the wild diet of the northwest woods, Billy had gone around like a father with his tongue curled with nerves and his very bowels queasy. On the journey homeward the baby had learned to stand, then to step, then to run laughing into Clark's arms. And at night, when the fiddle sang again and the men danced, thin and tattered as their own shadows, Pomp danced too, around and around among them, stamping his little moccasined feet.

So at the Mandan villages where Charbonneau was paid off, Clark came to Pomp's parents with the proposal he had been nursing.

"Let me have the boy," he urged them. "I will take him to the United States and bring him up in my own lodge. He shall be a great man some day, a great chief among the white chiefs." And they saw their captain look at them like a beggar.

Charbonneau fingered his beard and calculated. He had been to Montreal when he was young, and he understood something of what the offer meant. But Pomp decided it, unconsciously, when at this moment he flung himself against his mother and hung on to her fringed skirt, laughing up at her.

So she looked at Redhead with eyes that tried to tell him how a mother feels. She shook her head, and she made a hug of her arms to show how she must keep her baby still.

Even on the pirogue that left the Mandan villages, Clark wrote back, repeating his offer beseechingly. He never stopped working on Charbonneau till he got the little family in St. Louis, and, when the child was old enough, got Pomp started on an education.

By this time the tales that black York told, when he was liquored up, were long as Missouri and tall as the Rockies. He was a free man now, free to go to the devil in his own way, and he had plenty of company to rollick along with him, as he cut his way out of a grizzly's belly or single-handed carried the whole passel of white folks in a canoe over the rapids.

But always a million million leaves are sweeping from the tree. The blizzard winds of Russia tore down the Grand Army and scattered it forever. Russians, Austrians, Prussians soon appeared on the heights of Montmartre, and Josephine, swallowing her protests that she longed to follow the husband who had cast her off, into exile on Elba, rushed back from Navarre to give a party for her husband's conqueror. Among the royal guests she invited to honor the Czar that May evening was not only the King of Prussia but the Emperor of Austria who happened to be the father of Napoleon's second wife. Josephine's willfulness overrode everything. To-night, with the petty heroism of a great society leader, she put aside the distressful anxiety of her daughter Hortense, Queen of Holland.

"Of course, I am ill, wretchedly ill, but one must do one's duty," she feverishly cried.

And duty would now appear to be making the most of the Bourbons, who were the only ladder left, to say nothing of the Czar. So she opened the ball with Alexander and then took him for a promenade in the park, coughing away the night damps against the end of her filmy scarf. But czars and empresses are not impressive to septic angina.

It was to her empty shell at Malmaison, that costly trinket box, that Napoleon fled after Waterloo. He walked about the musty rooms fingering all the trifles and murmuring in feeble self-comfort to Hortense, "She really loved me, she really loved me . . ."

But those who took down every word he said on St. Helena cannot record that he ever spoke of her there. With half a year to live, he could remark, "St. Napoleon ought to be very much obliged to me, and do everything for me in the world to come. Poor fellow, nobody knew him before. He had not even a day in the calendar. I persuaded the Pope to give him my birthday."

Then, toward the end, as the cancer began to cut: "Why did the bullets spare my life, if it was only to lose it in this wretched way? Ah, what suffering! I feel at the left end of my stomach a pain that is unbearable, like the stab of a penknife."

On May second, 1821, he was babbling: "Desaix! Massena! Victory is ours. Go, haste, press home the charge; they are ours!" The next day, as the afternoon wore on, his lips formed words: "Head . . . army . . ." Then, after long, long minutes, the faint drums in his pulses beat the final retreat, and stopped.

Thomas Jefferson was then enjoying his Indian summer at Monticello. Those fields never saw so fair a harvest as his final years. Peacefully he lived along to the end. "I am like an old watch," he said at last, "with a pinion worn out here and a wheel there, until it can go no longer." And the serene smile lay like sunset on his face.

On the fourth of July, 1826, the fiftieth anniversary of the Declaration of Independence which he had penned, Thomas Jefferson died content.

We do not know how most of the members of the expedition left this life; they disappear; there is a line to record them here and there. One buys a farm, one marries, one goes off to war, one takes an ox-team and goes west again, to sow his seed in the Sacramento Valley. That was Willard, and you'll remember of him that he was flogged for sleeping on sentry duty, but he named one son Meriwether Lewis and another one William Clark, and with four sons and his own long musket he'd been to the Black Hawk War along with Abe Lincoln.

We seldom know just when and where each leaf descends. We never hear what happened to Cruzatte, who drifts from our sight like foam on the Missouri, or to stout Ordway, though it is to be imagined that his last days were deservedly happy, among his rich orchards and farmlands in the Twywappitty Bottom.

Ten years after Jefferson's death, Clark learned that Judge George Shannon had dropped dead in court. To the aging Clark, it seemed like heavy news. He had lost touch now with the last of them; even Sacajawea and Pomp were gone, he knew not where. He had heard that Charbonneau had struck her once too often, this time at the instigation of a new young wife, and Sacajawea had walked forth from his roof, free at last because her son, grown a man, no longer needed a father.

That son of a red woman spent six astonishing years in Europe, guest of his patron the Prince of Württemberg. Prince Paul was a notable explorer of the American Northwest, and Baptiste became his guide. The educated halfbreed spoke now half a dozen Indian languages, and English, French, German, and Spanish besides; he was slight, wiry, graceful, handsome, marked with an aristocracy he did not get from his trader father. Kit Carson, Jim Bridger, General Cooke—they knew him; they prized him. He found the water-holes and the passes; he could smell an ambush from afar; he could fight like a devil and, they say, sat forty hours once at a deck of euchre.

The snows drive and the springs come. The buffalo

are going; the red men are dying; they are surrounded and driven as they drove the antelope. Presidents come and go. In the South the black men multiply; the black cloud of war gathers and darkens. In the West the flag of the United States is pressing toward California, toward Oregon; there is a slow creak of wagon wheels on the long trails. But William Clark dies without ever hearing of Sacajawea again, without ever forgetting that once when they were starving at Fort Clatsop she gave him a piece of bread she had been saving for her baby.

Summers come and autumns pass over his honored grave, and still no word of her. No one knows where she has gone, and there is almost no one left to ask. Cameahwait has fallen in battle against the Pah-kes; honest old Bratton is buried in Waynetown; the snows cover him, and the spring comes back, and does not inquire.

But General Frémont, with his guide Kit Carson riding beside him, sights in the trackless plains an Indian woman. They overtake her, and see that she is leading two little girls, one a waif that she has found upon the road, and the other her own, Crying Basket, the child of her last fecundity. The face lifted to the two horsemen was still comely, with a fine dignity on it. She wore a Comanche dress, and Kit Carson spoke to her in that language. She said her name was Porivo, which means "Chief" in Comanche.

"But I am not Comanche," said Porivo, "I am Shoshone. My Comanche husband is dead, killed in battle. I have left our son Ticanef with the tribe, to take his place. I am hunting for my own people now. I am hunting for my son, Baptiste."

"Would he be the one they call Charbonneau?" asked Carson. "Yes? Well, then, Porivo, I can tell you where he is. He is with Jim Bridger in the South Pass. And all the Shoshones have come down there to live, on the Green River. You come along with us, Porivo. We're going a piece of that way, and we'll let you ride our horses, you and these children."

She thanked them, and accepted. That night when they made camp, she went off with a sharp stick to dig yampah roots, wild fennel, because it is a squaw's business to do this, and the white men didn't know good food when they saw it. They'd starve with plenty around them, because they didn't know what any squaw knows.

Frémont watched her in the starry dusk, her sturdy figure industriously bending and digging, and he called her in his diary "a Naomi hunting for her people." He was a cultivated man, was John Charles Frémont, who knew his classics, but he did not recognize the guest he entertained that night, and neither did the Indian-wise Kit Carson.

The sand and the snow, they cover all trails. The sagebrush bends but leaves no trace. Now the terrible thorn of slavery must be plucked from the festering side of the nation; now the forces of disunion rack the body of the people. Lincoln is elected; Sumter is fired on and surrenders; Bull Run is fought and lost. Now they will break your beautiful union, Thomas Jefferson, George Washington, old Abe, unless every man who can bear arms steps up to defend it.

The recruiting sergeant at Wellsburg, West Virginia, opened his eyes and mouth and gagged on a laugh. But with his one eye Pat Gass overlooked this, as he brought his antique musket up to his shoulder.

"How old are you, Grandsir?" marveled the sergeant not unkindly.

"What in the name of all the saints has that got to do with it?" demanded Patrick. "I'm a hot Democrat, and I lost this eye at Lundy's Lane, by God. I wasn't too old when I married at sixty to get me seven children, and I'm not too old at ninety to shoot at the seat of Johnny Reb's pants."

"Well, now, sir," gently said the sergeant, "looks to me, if you fought in the War in 1812, you've done your part for the country."

"I did that," said Pat Gass with ancient relish, "when I went west to the Pacific in 1804 with Captain Lewis and Captain Clark."

Of all the men who went, he was the last to die. For years before he married, he'd been a drunkard and a wastrel—or as much of a wastrel as a man can be on a government pension of ninety-six dollars a year—but in his ninety-ninth year he got ready for God. The whole town of Wellsburg crowded on the banks of the Ohio, to sing "Shall We Gather at the River" and watch old man Gass get baptized in the icy flood. So when he went, he went in grace and glory.

Now the grass is deep over the graves at Fredericksburg. Now the swallows return to their nests at the bluffs of Shiloh. There is peace among the states, and peace between the Mormons and the Gentiles. The Union Pacific Railroad is building east from San Francisco; going west from Omaha, it has got as far as Fort Bridger, in July of 1868. Climbing up over the sagebrush plains, it has reached the South Pass where the snows glitter on the Uintahs and Wasatches. When it gets down through the pass it will strike for Salt Lake City.

So it was time, plainly, to move the Shoshones off this land below the South Pass, for white settlers would soon be demanding sections along the gleaming rails. There was need, too, of some buffer state against the Teton Sioux who were still hanging like a hornet cloud over Wyoming between the Bighorns and the Black Hills. Let that friendly nation be the Shoshones who had so early made their peace with the whites.

"The question is," murmured General William Tecumseh Sherman, wiping the Fourth of July sweat from a brow marked with the army hatband, "will they sign the treaty? After all, we can't make them move up to the Wind River valley and expose their flank to the Sioux, without fighting them if they refuse." He looked around him at the massed and silent Indians in the council, and then worriedly back at Judge William Carter, Chief Inhabitant of little Fort Bridger. "By the looks of this fellow Washakie," he muttered, "we'd find him a warrior tough as the Sioux themselves."

"Listen to Washakie, General," replied Judge Carter. "He's a statesman as well as a warrior, the finest Indian I've ever met."

A long wind came over the sagebrush and lifted Washakie's words to float and ring above the heads of the silent tribes.

"I want for our home the valley of the Wind River," the chief was saying, "but the Sioux may trouble us there. They must be driven away. The whites must help us do this."

In the strong harsh voice General Sherman heard both warning and appeal, and he saw the eagle feathers quiver all down the erect old back.

"Are his people with him?" anxiously whispered the general to Carter, watching the unresponsive Indian faces.

The fierce sun beat upon this sage that was Shoshone terrain, and the white men felt very few and foreign, even Carter. It's touch and go, he thought forebodingly, and his intent frown said as much to the soldier.

Out of the squatting many-colored ranks of the women then arose one. She walked forward with the step of one who can go anywhere. She was a small woman, eighty years old, but she stood commandingly against the wind, in the circle of red men and white, both her people. Her names ran in a murmur on the lips of all: "Went-a-Long-Way," "Lost Woman," "Constant Lover," "Porivo," "Canoe Launcher," "Sacajawea!"

Then she spoke. The wind upheld her reedy voice, and Carter, straining like the Indians to hear, caught words and phrases: "Shoshone people, there is nothing that does not change . . . Soon the buffalo will all be gone. The Indians must learn to live like the white men and beside the white men . . . I have seen great fields where our white friends grow sweet corn. They know how to make the rivers run in ditches, to keep the land always green. So they keep their cattle fat. They eat the good meat of them; they milk the cows, and drink the milk. They make the land give greatly to them . . . Let us go to the Wind River valley, as the Whites are asking us to do. Let us learn to plant their good seeds, and how to turn the rivers to our will. It is not true that the gophers will come out of their burrows and stare at us till we die, because we have made water run uphill. That is the chatter of foolish birds. Listen instead to the white men. I have known them long and long. Theirs is a great nation, the greatest. It marches always forward, in ways of peace and plenty. I have seen this. Now I have spoken."

At sixteen she had not been too young to guide that nation; at eighty she was not too old to speed it on its way.

So the Shoshones sowed and planted, at the foot of the Wind River range, white with snows as Sacajawea's head. The green alfalfa grew where once was only desert, and the honeybee came to the clover. Sacajawea's grandchildren and great-grandchildren ran about the reservation, fat and friendly. Her son Baptiste was beside her again, gone back to the blanket, with three wives to share it. Basil, too, was with her, the boy she had made her own at the Lemhi pass, a man now much respected. He had led his Shoshones to the aid of the whites when, under General Crook, they had crushed the Sioux forever. So the Americans, aborigines too, were at peace. The years ran swift and level as the water in the irrigation ditches.

They say, those still living who remember her, that the reservation store would never take money from Sacajawea. But a man remembers that he tried to pay her, for some blankets she had made, with paper money, and that she returned it politely. "Young man, you cannot fool me," she kindly said. "I knew well great white chiefs who died long before you were born. It was not with paper that those men of honor paid."

She still had her wits about her; she still had her strength. Another man relates that he saw her get down to shoulder a pack which must have weighed sixty pounds. "Grandmother," he protested, "that is too much for you to tote!" But she got to her feet under the load without staggering, for all her ninety-odd years, and she looked at him with an ancient amusement and did not tell him, in his ignorance, of what she had carried when she was a girl, and how far she had carried it.

The nights of April, in 1884, were cold, in that high place under the snowy mountains. In Wyoming April is so faintly spring that it is like a spring remembered from long ago. The little house next to the agency on the Wind River reservation was a tidy place, a story and a half high; that was where old Sacajawea lived. The last of the firelight in that house flickered out late in the night, in the first hours of April the ninth. There in the great darkness lay Sacajawea, wrapped in her shake-down of quilts and blankets, a little brown kernel within its husks.

You cannot look at a seed and say just when it has ceased to live. They found her in the morning without breath in her nostrils, and they called her dead.

But the seed that is a human spirit is viable forever. It is not only what she did that lives, but what she was. For she was the one who foresaw the way, who pointed out the passes, who all her life kept faith with the nation she forwarded. Reward she never got; what could we have given her better than she had in herself?

It was she who gave, liberal as earth, to her captains, to her children, her people, our own, and now to our-selves. For the thought of her still lifts the eyes up, from the stones before our feet, to find a way to the shining mountains, a hard way but a right one. It is for us to be brave enough and strong enough to take it.

The last resting places of the Shoshone chiefs on the reservation are marked with war lances and pennants of faded colors, but at her head white men have raised a small monument with a bronze tablet identifying her: "Sacajawea, a guide with the Lewis and Clark expedition." The way to this grave is worn by the footsteps of the white men still following her.

They have named for her a peak in the Wind River range, one of the highest in all the West. The snows never fade on its sharp summit, but when they melt a little, in the high brief summer, the alpine wildflowers spring up at the foot of these glaciers. All her life, it is told, she worshiped mountain flowers. It is recorded that she said, "They are the spirits of those children whose footsteps have passed from the earth, but reappear each spring to gladden the pathway of those now living."

THE SOURCES

THERE ARE three great, and more or less distinct editions of the journals of Lewis and Clark. The first is the *History of the Expedition under the Command of Captains Lewis and Clark,* 2 vols. (Philadelphia, 1814.) This is known as the Biddle edition, having been put out by the aid and under the general direction of Nicholas Biddle, though an editor named Paul Allen (of whom nothing has ever since been heard) has his name on the title page. This work was prepared after Lewis's death, but during the lifetime of Clark, who read it all and gave substantial aid from his memory. George Shannon, one of the best educated of the men on the expedition, was at Biddle's side; his ear for Indian languages, as well as his fresh young memory for events so recently lived, were, Biddle wrote Clark, invaluable. So this edition is a composite narrative, derived from Lewis's and Clark's original field notes and from the diary of Sergeant Whitehouse, who sold it to the captains at the end of the voyage. Shannon is said to have kept a diary also, and this would doubtless have been at hand at the time. Thomas Jefferson wrote the introduction, together with a memoir of Lewis.

The Biddle edition is therefore of immense value; it makes very smooth reading, since discrepancies between the diarists' notes are harmonized, mistakes of many sorts corrected, prolix material excised, and Indian words made uniform. It suffers, however, from the defects of these virtues. It is a smoothed-out work, from which personality has been ironed away. Also it suffers from the exclusion of the remarkable scientific notes on Indian life, on animals, vegetation, geography, mineralogy—all of which it had been the intention of Clark and Jefferson to reserve for careful editing and final publication in scientific journals—publication that never took place.

The Biddle edition has been many times reprinted, sometimes in the best of style and again in pirated or variously mangled or vulgarized catch-penny reprints.

It was disgust for the omission of the precious scientific material that made the famous naturalist Elliott Coues undertake a new edition. This bore the title of the Biddle edition, but was printed in four volumes in New York, 1893. In it Coues followed the Biddle text but appended thousands of footnotes including a great part of the neglected scientific materials, together with many direct extracts from the original notebooks of the two explorers, and with others from the journals of Whitehouse and Gass. Coues, himself a veteran explorer of the Northwest, traversed most of the Lewis and Clark route, and he carefully correlates their campsites, river names, and landmarks with the same places and place-names found today.

The Coues edition is therefore of great interest, since the editor was himself a man of wide cultivation and a highly specialized knowledge of the environment. He adds a memoir of William Clark and a discussion of the circumstances surrounding Lewis's death by violence.

But it remained for the distinguished historian Reuben Gold Thwaites, in 1905, to issue the *Original Journals of the Lewis and Clark Expedition* in 8 volumes, with all the drawings and maps made by the explorers themselves, together with a wealth of biographical and statistical material. This stupendous work gives the original notes of the two leaders, the original Floyd and Whitehouse diaries, and a mass of correspondence, among Lewis, Jefferson, Clark, and others.

This, then, becomes the definitive edition of the Lewis and Clark journals. In it, they stand in all their imperfections which, however, amount in themselves to a sort of final perfection. For they reveal the journey just as it was lived, endured, viewed, by its chief actors. And they reveal the characters of these men as nothing else has ever done. Unfortunately it is a very costly work, and so voluminous that it is only mastered by students.

More recently two new journals have come to light—Lewis's narrative of his journey from Pittsburg to the camp on Wood River, before the expedition really started, and Sergeant Ordway's daily log. These two have been reprinted under the editorship of Milo M. Quaife, in the *Collections* of the State Historical Society of Wisconsin, vol. xxii (Madison, 1916) under the title *The Journals of Captain Meriwether Lewis and Sergeant John Ordway*. Lewis's narrative is incomplete, about a month being lost, and is of interest chiefly as showing Lewis's first trials of his boat, and of river navigation. Ordway's record, though that of a literal-minded man of no great education, is still a sterling one. Alone among all the diarists of the expedition, he never missed a single day. He fills in every gap, and on the return journey, his account is in one considerable stretch our only authority for the events that took place.

First in point of view of publication, but perhaps last in importance, comes Gass's account, published in 1807 (before the official Biddle account) and reprinted in 1904 under the editorship of James Hosmer. There is no question that

Sergeant Patrick Gass was a lively, observant, full-blooded fellow, whose original document, however illiterate, would have been good reading. Unfortunately he turned his text over to a schoolteacher for editing, and this well-intentioned dominie proceeded to delete large portions of it and to render the rest in the most stilted and unlifelike English, thereby turning *Gass's Journal* from a precious document into a complete mediocrity.

There have been numerous commentaries on the Expedition. Such are N. Brooks, *First Across the Continent: Expedition of Lewis and Clark* (New York, 1901) and James K. Hosmer, *The Expedition of Lewis and Clark*. Highly interesting and well illustrated is *The Trail of Lewis and Clark* by Olin D. Wheeler, 2 vols. (New York, 1904), which discusses in detail the countryside through which Lewis and Clark passed, right from Wood River in Illinois, to the mouth of the Columbia and back again, with highly valuable notes on the Indians and the geography of the country as it was then, correlated with the same region at the beginning of this century.

No biographies of Lewis and Clark have ever been written. Lewis's short life, in which he communicated so little of himself, may always remain closed to complete biography, though there is a good account of him in the *Dictionary of American Biography*. William Clark's longer career and more ebullient personality might still furnish forth materials for a full-length portrait.

But of the scant historical traces of Sacajawea there exists, fortunately, a very brilliant study by Prof. Grace R. Hebard: *Sacajawea, a guide and interpreter of the Lewis and Clark Expedition, with an account of the travels of Toussaint Charbonneau and of Jean Baptiste, the expedition papoose* (Glendale, California, 1933). A number of persons share the honor of proving that the Indian woman who died in 1884 on the Wind River Reservation of the Shoshone Indians was the same who, as a girl of sixteen and seventeen, had so long ago guided the illustrious explorers. But among them none deserves more credit than Prof. Hebard, who traced out the wanderings of Sacajawea and the strange adventures of her child for the seventy years that Sacajawea lived after parting with the expedition. The originality of this historian's work is truly remarkable and the present author acknowledges a large debt to her.

He is indebted also to Mr. Wayne Johnson of Butte, Montana, who placed in his hands an unpublished manuscript of his which has unique value. It consists in a series of more than a hundred superb photographs of the campsites of Lewis and Clark, from Great Falls to the spot where the expedition constructed their boats for descent of the Columbia. The photographs are accompanied by the pertinent extracts from the journals of the explorers, together with comment on the localities. This highly valuable document has been indispensable to the present writer, since Mr. Johnson's familiarity with the Montana and Idaho country is life-long, and he penetrated portions of the expedition's trail which the author of the present volume did not succeed in reaching on his own journeys in the great footsteps.